The
TORTOISE & TURTLE
FEEDING
MANUAL

New Expanded Edition

By A. C. Highfield

Carapace Press
London

THE TORTOISE AND TURTLE FEEDING MANUAL

Text © 1988-2000 A. C. Highfield
Photographs © 2000 A. C. Highfield
All rights reserved

This edition first published 2000

ISBN 1 873943 23 7

Published and distributed by
Carapace Press UK and USA

Visit our website for latest titles

www.vidi-herp.com

For additional information on tortoise and turtle care
please visit the Tortoise Trust website at
www.tortoisetrust.org

Or write:
Tortoise Trust
BM Tortoise
London
WC1N 3XX
England

Notes on Dietary Constituents for Herbivorous Terrestrial Chelonians and their effect on Growth and Development

A C Highfield

(This article was originally published in 1988 by the Association for the Study of Reptiles and Amphibians. At the time of original publication, most tortoise organizations were recommending high protein diets including dog and cat food. The research which prompted this article was undertaken in response to the high number of deformed and dying tortoises seen which had been subjected to this dietary regime. This new edition contains an updated text)

Introduction

Dietary related disorders represent a major cause of mortality in captive bred hatchlings and juveniles (Highfield 1986, Zwart 1987). Lambert (1986, 1988) reported that the median survivorship of UK captive bred *Testudo graeca* is 1.5 years, that of *T. hermanni* 1.75 years and *T. marginata* 2.3 years but does not provide any clinical reason for such mortalities other than to indicate that growth rates are more rapid than those attained in the wild, and that carapace deformities are characteristic of such animals. These median survivorship figures agree with those recorded by the present author from submissions made by members of the public and other inexperienced keepers. Detailed examination of the affected living and deceased specimens reveals that a combination of recognized clinical factors are invariably present, principally acute secondary nutritional osteodystrophy resulting from and inadequate dietary Ca:P ratio (Wallach and Hoessele, 1968) frequently combined with hepatic dysfunction and renal dysfunction urea and deposits of uric acid within the renal tubules. The latter condition is most often observed in cases where artificially high protein diets have been imposed by keepers upon herbivorous species which in their native habitat would experience much lower levels of dietary protein. High incidences of renal and hepatic disease have been noted for some time both in veterinary reports and necropsy surveys of long-term captive chelonians. Keymer's survey of 1978 which details the result of 144 pathological examinations reports that G.I. tract, hepatic and renal disease accounted respectively for 27%, 11% and 9.7% of mortalities with miscellaneous nutritional disorders contributing a further 22.2% of the total. 77.8% of the study group had been housed in the London Zoo, the remainder being drawn from animals belonging to members of the public (Keymer, 1978).

A second survey by Rosskopf drew exclusively upon animals which had been maintained as pets. In this survey the findings were that 72.6% of mortalities exhibited severe hepatic disorders, 53% respiratory disease (principally pneumonia), 50.7% G.1 tract disorders, 40.6% renal disease and 34.3% cardiac dysfunction (Rosskopf, 1981). It is notable that in both surveys gastrointestinal disorders are particularly significant (with parasites accounting for some, but not all of these), and that the incidence of hepatic and renal disease is much higher in animals which have been maintained principally as pets. A currently unpublished survey of tortoises originating from pet keepers and subsequently acquired by the Tortoise Trust also reveals a high incidence of renal and hepatic disease. It is interesting to note that captive herbivorous iguanas often display almost identical nutritional disorders (Wallach and Hoessele, 1968, 1966).

Nutritional Disorders

The disorders may be usefully divided into two main groups consisting of:

a)   diseases of excess
b)   diseases of deficiency

Clinically, combinations of the two groups are common, e.g., acute carapace distortion due to lack of dietary calcium and concurrent hepatic and renal dysfunction resulting from dangerously high consumption of saturated fats, proteins and nitrates.

In practice, it is possible to achieve a combination of normal growth and satisfactory osteological carapace development without incurring the mortality noted by Lambert provided adequate attention is given to the specific dietary requirements of the species concerned and that sufficient levels of all essential trace elements are present (Highfield, 1988). The dietary factor is of considerably more significance to growth and development that climatological influences, although the latter is frequently of great importance with regard to initiation of the breeding cycle (Reiter and Follett, 1980; Vivien-Roels, Arendt and Bradtke, 1979).

Dietary Calcium

The calcium requirement of chelonians is variable and increases during growth phases and in the case of females during egg formation. Given that a 100% growth-weight increase frequently occurs during the first eight weeks of life, it is clear that this period is especially critical. The calcium requirement is also dependent upon external factors such as the quantity of dietary phosphorous. Vitamin D3 availability is also of relevance. In the wild, tortoises from desert habitats typically experience a calcium to phosphorous ratio of between 5: 1 to 8: 1. The greater proportion of plants consumed are richer in calcium than they are in phosphorous, are comparatively low in protein and are also high in fiber. Furthermore, additional trace elements are consumed as soil, sand and grit particles. Zwart (1987) notes that a critical Ca:P deficiency ratio of 1.2:1 is typical and that at this level osteoporosis and osteomalacia (softshell syndrome) together with other deformities of the scutes recorded by Lambert (1983) manifest. Supplementation with Vionate (Ciba-Geigy) is frequently inadequate, as this product itself contains both calcium and phosphorous in the ratio of 2:1, and excess phosphorous in the principal diet rapidly reduces the ratio actually attained to critical deficiency levels. Certain food items used by some captive breeders are particularly disruptive of the calcium balance, especially legumes, sprouting seeds and processed cat or dog food of animal origin. This latter frequently has a negative Ca:P ratio by as much as 1:44 or more (Collins, 1971), whilst 100g of peas typically contains 42 mg Ca to 127 mg P, broad beans 27 mg Ca to 160 mg P and mung sprouts 19 mg Ca to 64 mg P.

The high phytic acid content of legumes, specifically peas and beans, which impedes Ca is also cause for concern. Each of these items has in the past been recommended as a suitable substitute item for inclusion in the diet of hatching chelonians. Lettuce, which is frequently condemned as a dietary constituent, is in fact relatively neutral in the Ca:P sense, ranging from 20 mg Ca to 22 mg P/100g in the case of Iceberg varieties, to 68 mg Ca to 25 mg P/100g for Romaine varieties. Although inadequate alone, it is useful neutral base for further controlled artificial supplementation. Another common tortoise food item, dandelion, is of extremely high quality comprising 187 mg Ca to 66 mg P/100g and combining this with 14,000 iu Vitamin-A, 1. 6g fiber, 0 - 19 mg thiamine and 2.7g protein. Banana fruit and leaves which are frequently utilized in tropical captive breeding projects as a readily obtainable staple dietary item are strongly Ca:P negative and liable to induce a relative Ca deficiency in rapidly growing animals (typically 8 mg Ca to 30 mg P/100g fresh, 32 mg Ca to 104 mg P/100g dried).

4

Some food items which appear initially to represent good sources of dietary calcium are not as attractive on closer examination. Beet greens, kale, spinach and members of the Goosefoot family *Chenopodiaceae* contain relatively high Ca levels but this is bound up with oxalic acid which reacts with calcium to form insoluble calcium oxalate. *Opuntia* cacti, a typical food item of arid habitat tortoises including *Gopherus agassizi and Geochelone elephantopus* offers by comparison 1.89% calcium to 0.02% phosphorous (Rosskopf, 1982). Other self-selected native food items of *G. agassizi* reveal similarly positive Ca:P ratios.

The dietary preferences of *T. hermanni* and *T. graeca* in the wild have seldom been recorded, notable exceptions being the work of Swingland (1984) and Stubbs who noted that 25% of the diet of *T. hermanni* consisted of *Rubiaceae* (Bedstraw family), 22% of *Leguminosae* (Peaflower family), 10% *of Compositae* (Daisy family) and *80% Ranunculaceae* (Buttercup family). Comparative figures for *T. graeca* include 30% *Plantago* (Plantain family), 26% *Compositae and 10% Rubiaceae*. An average Ca:P ratio for the above is 3.5:1, and a typical protein content is 2.75% (Highfield, unpublished notes). More recent work by Cobo and Andreu (1988) provides a detailed analysis of the diet of *T. g. graeca* in Spain. This latter publication is invaluable as it reveals, for the first time, highly detailed breakdowns of plant species consumed and average daily intakes. The average fresh weight of food consumed by adults was 71.4g (dry weight 6.28g).

A practical solution in captivity is to botanically screen all dietary items carefully and exclude items which are strongly Ca:P negative from regular consumption. The remaining neutral or positive Ca:P constituents can then be supplemented with a multi-vitamin and mineral powder boosted if necessary by the addition of raw calcium lactate until a true ratio of at least 5:1 is achieved. In practice, hatchling *T. graeca, Geochelone pardalis* and *Geochelone carbonaria* raised on such a regime do not display the deformed carapaces and raised vertebral shields so typical of nutritional secondary osteodystrophy fibrosa which were remarked upon by Lambert (1986) and which results from an excess growth of keratin combined with the sub-optimum development of the underlying bony plates.

Vitamin D and Ultraviolet Light

Animals in their natural habitat are extremely unlikely to suffer hypovitaminosis-D3. Deficiencies are possible in captive animals which are deprived of access to sunlight or a suitable artificial U.V. source of sufficient intensity, e.g. True-lite, Zoomed 2.0-5.0, or blacklight. Symptoms of deficiency include poor locomotion, osteomalacia and osteoporosis. Plant foods contain nil vitamin D. The skin of tortoises is however, extremely rich in oils containing sterols which react with U.V. to produce the vitamin and provided adequate U.V. exposure is attained oral supplementation is not necessary (Kauffield, 1969; Wagner, 1977). It is common for herpetologists to over estimate D3 demand and to grossly overdose orally. One possible consequence of this practice is metastatic mineralization of the soft tissues (Barten, 1982; Wallach and Hoessle, 1966). Vitamin D3 is highly toxic and extreme caution should be exercised whenever oral supplementation is employed (Finlayson and Woods, 1977). If calcium and phosphorous are provided in suitable ratios and sufficient quantity and quality of U.V. are available, hypovitaminosis D3 is not at all likely. Human demand is for 10 micrograms (400 iu) per day which can be obtained from as little as 3 hours exposure to sunlight. The requirements of tortoises are not known in detail, although Zwart (1987) suggest that 10-20,000 iu of D3 per Kg of general vitamin-mineral supplement dosed routinely at 4% food volume is an effective prophylactic measure where exposure to U.V. is inadequate.

Hypovitaminosis-B

B complex deficiencies have been recorded by the author in both hatchling and adult *T. graeca and T. kleinmanni* where animals have been maintained by owners on what amount to lettuce-only diets. The B group includes thiamine riboflavin, pyridoxine, nicotinic acid, pantothenic acid, biotin, folic acid and cobalamin. Clinical signs of deficiency include lack of neuromuscular coordination and pernicious anaemia. In the wild, it is probable that tortoises are able to obtain adequate levels of B12 to interact with dietary folic acid by gut microflora activity involving trace dietary cobalt. B12 is absent in vegetation, but essential to life. Although it has been recommended by some herpetologists (Reid, 1982; Engberg, 1980) raw fish is categorically not suitable dietary constituent for terrestrial chelonians due to its high protein level and thiaminase content which prevents synthesis and absorption of B-group vitamins. Deficiency is particularly common following severe colitis and malabsorbtion syndrome resulting from pathogenic flagellate infection of the gastrointestinal tract.

Dietary Iodine

Fibrous goiter or hypothyroidism is commonplace among captive herbivorous chelonians, particularly *G. elephantopus* and *G. gigantea* maintained in zoological collections and which have been fed diets rich in vegetables containing high levels of anionic goitrogens (e. g., glucosinolates and thiocyanates) such as cabbage and kale. The condition has also been observed in hatchling *T. graeca* and *T. marginata* subjected to an identical dietary regime. The consumption of the responsible class of vegetables needs to be limited and in addition a multi-mineral supplement containing traces of iodine at a suggested dose rate of 6-10 mg per Kg of supplement should by routinely provided with every meal. Vegetation from mountainous areas, or from soil rich in limestone may be lower than average in dietary iodine.

Dietary Fat

A disease of excess, steatitis or fatty infiltration of the liver is encountered frequently in captive chelonians and is an established cause of mortality in both hatchlings and in adults (Will, 1975; Rosskopf, 1981). Herbivorous chelonians are poorly equipped to metabolize saturated fats (Tammar, 1974), and when subjected to high fat content diets develop serious hepatosis resulting in jaundice and the inability to retain vitamin-A; hence hypovitaminosis-A is often concurrent clinically with steatitis. In the wild, virtually no saturated fats whatsoever are consumed, yet in captivity many keepers habitually provide dietary sources which are extremely rich in these substances. *Tinned cat and dog foods are undoubtedly the worst offenders in this respect.* Taking into account the normally reduced metabolic rate of most captive animals compared with wild specimens due to reduced temperatures and photo-periods, it is therefore not surprising that many mortalities are found post mortem to be suffering from obesity and gross fatty lesions of the liver. Botanical analysis of the native diet of *T. graeca and G. agassizi* which may be assumed typical for species inhabiting similar biotypes, indicate that an average level of polyunsaturated fat consumption is 0.35g per 100g of raw vegetation. Existing cases of steatitis may respond to veterinary treatment with thyroxine and vitamin-E.

Dietary Protein

Captive chelonians are frequently placed on diets richer in useable protein by a factor of several magnitudes greater than they would possibly be able to attain in the wild, and this, combined with a lack of dietary calcium is a major direct cause of mortalities in the median of 1.5 to 1.75 age group. The growth of such specimens is greatly accelerated, and full sexual maturity has been observed by the author in one captive bred male *T. graeca ibera* at just 19 months of age. This animal weighed 565g and had a carapace length of 148 mm. There was marked carapace deformity and overgrowth of keratin, the beak being extremely overgrown to the extent of interfering with normal feeding.

Similar observations have been made in respect of *Gopherus agassizi* hatchlings captive-bred in the USA, when calcium deficient protein-rich diets of vegetable origin were employed to rear hatchlings by amateur herpetologists instead of a diet of designed to replicate as closely as possible the naturally occurring diet of the species (Jackson and

6

Trotter, 1976; Hansen, Johnson, Van Devender 1976). The photographs illustrating the first reference show grossly deformed carapaces typical of the most acute form of nutritional osteodystrophy fibrosa.

In addition to stimulating excessive growth, both generally and of the keratin in particular thus increasing the calcium demand yet further, the intake of high levels of protein has two further effects a) there is a direct effect upon calcium absorption ability (Margen, 1974) and b) high protein results in high levels of blood urea and consequently increases the amount of nitrogenous waste to be processed via the renal system. Unfortunately, reliable data on blood urea nitrogen and creatinine levels of wild populations is not readily available and most studies so far published have relied upon data extracted from captive specimens, mostly pet animals belonging to members of the public (e.g., see Rosskopf, 1982). Although useful, this data is unlikely to represent a true picture of the normal blood chemistry of specimens in the native habitat. It is not at all unusual for herbivorous chelonians which have been maintained on unnaturally high protein diets to exhibit symptoms of renal dysfunction. Dehydrated animals are obviously most at risk, as the accumulated uric acid becomes deposited not only in the renal tubules but invasively throughout the pericardium, liver and other organs (Frye, 1974; Wallach, 1971). Specific conditions recorded include interstitial nephrosis and glomerulosclerosis (Rosskopf, 1981). Once again, processed tinned pet foods of animal origin are particularly dangerous as not only are they high in protein (typically 17%) and saturated fats, rich in phosphorous and relatively low in calcium but most are also very rich in other nitrates. Cheese, another item which has seriously been suggested as an appropriate dietary component for *T. graeca* is similarly adverse in effect (protein content typically 25%). Legumes are also spectacularly high in protein for a vegetable source (typically 10%), and should be avoided for the same reasons.

The protein requirement for most reptiles have not been studied in sufficient detail and specific figures have not been widely established for herbivorous terrestrial chelonians. Analysis of the native diet of *G. agassizi*, which in many respects is typical of and habitat chelonian herbivores, suggests that the protein content of the food intake ranges from 1% *(Opuntia sp.*) with grasses at a median content of 5% constituting a major part of the dietary intake (Rosskopf, 1982; Hansen et al, 1976). A safe upper protein limit for items which are regularly included in the diet would seem to be 7% as this is about as high as is ever attained in the wild by most species, even during peak periods of food availability. An average intake level of 4% would represent a close approximation of that experienced in the natural habitat. All percentages are cited in 'wet' weight form.

Despite the lack of detailed information on protein demand, it is certain that the figure is very much lower Kg for Kg than mammals where 0.5g of usable protein per Kg would be a typical daily requirement. It seems probable that the daily requirement of a growing tortoise is in the approximate region of 0.20g of usable protein per Kg, although this may well vary considerably according to species and metabolic rate. Against this it should be noted that even such a low quality food item as lettuce contains an average of 1g per 100g and most legumes contain well in excess of 7g/100g.

In the wild tortoises consume not only plant leaf material, but also seeds, fruits, flowers, roots, bark and grasses. See Samour, Spratt, Hart, Savage and Hawkey (1987) for an excellent survey which conveys the scale of the dietary eclecticism of *Geochelone gigantea,* for example. The principal importance of this varied intake is not merely that it provides a relatively wide range of vitamins, minerals and fiber, but that by combining leaf, bark grass and seed sources an improved range of essential amino-acids is made available in a complementary process. This has the effect of increasing the potential Net Protein Utilization (NPU) factor of the diet. Where tortoises are provided with a suitable intake of essential amino-acids derived from the correct balance of vegetable matter they can exist perfectly satisfactorily on diets which are surprisingly low (in percentage terms) of protein content. Artificial amino-acid supplementation is not necessary provided a reasonable range of suitable food items are available although this has sometimes been adopted (Bacon, 1980). **In most captive situations pathology results consistently indicate that it is protein excess rather than deficiency which is the principal danger.** Meat based products have an extremely high NPU as they represent a complete amino acid source. 100g of dog food containing 15% protein is, therefore, utilized at a greater rate than a vegetable containing an equivalent percentage of raw protein. In some circumstances and with some reptiles this may be of benefit, in the case of herbivores it is entirely inappropriate. The diet of a wild tortoise typically contains between 2%-6% plant protein which is utilized at an approximate rate of 55%. The high protein regimes adopted by some herpetologists for herbivorous chelonians include up to 20% protein which, because it is derived from amino-acid complete sources is utilized at a typical rate of 70%.

It is necessary to comment upon the claim often made that terrestrial chelonians from and habitats receive significant additional protein in the wild as a result of consuming carrion, arthropods and other insects. This is not supported by fecal pellet analysis (Dearden, Hansen and Steinhorst, 1974) which indicates that such intake is so low as to be of virtually nil dietary significance. The levels parlleled that of other miscellaneous detritus also consumed, including small rocks, sand, bird feathers, lizard skin casts and mammal hairs (Hansen et al, 1976). Most tortoises will consume anything which is presented to them whether palatable and nutritious or not. Until separated from the public by barriers, giant tortoises at San Diego zoo were known to consume popcorn, balloons, yogurt, film wrappers, chewing gum and red-painted toenails (Bacon, 1980). Habitat analysis suggests that animals from and areas would not frequently encounter available sources of animal protein, but that animals from more humid habitats may have greater opportunities in this respect. Certainly, some *T. hermanni* may occasionally display an inclination to consume a passing slug or worm, but they make no effort to actively seek out such delicacies. In experiments conducted by the author most Mediterranean tortoises showed no interest whatsoever in slugs, worms or insects presented to them and indeed demonstrated active avoidance behavior in many instances. The exception was *T. hermanni*, which has been observed to take the occasional snail and worm in wet weather.

The Role of Symbiotic Digestive Microflora

The intestinal microflora of herbivorous chelonians is geared to processing relatively large quantities of fibrous, carbohydrate-rich cellulose matter. There is reason to suppose that protozoans and ciliate organisms play a role in this process together with the more unusual bacterial agents (see Fenchel, McRoy, Ogden, Parker and Rainey, 1979). Non-specific enteritis is common in captive collections (Keymer, 1978; Hunt, 1957) ac counting for up to 40% of total mortalities in some cases. Deficiencies of dietary fiber are certainly one factor (Shaw, 1961; Throp, 1969; Bacon, 1980) and an adequate intake of dietary fiber may also be of importance in regulating populations of potentially pathogenic parasites. An additional factor responsible for the high incidence of gastrointestinal disease noted may be inclusion of food items of animal origin to which the slow fermentation process of the herbivores digestive system appears ill suited (Bellairs, 1969; Holt, 1978; Dandifrosse, 1974; Sokol, 1967; Skoczylas, 1978).

Conclusions

The dietary requirements of captive herbivorous chelonians are far more complex than has previously been assumed by many keepers. It is apparent that the simplistic approach of providing a *high quality* diet in mammalian terms is totally inadequate to meet the real needs of chelonians which have a completely different set of requirements. Indeed, that which may represent a high quality diet for a mammal or carnivorous reptile may have entirely negative consequences when presented to a chelonian herbivore.

REFERENCES

Bacon, J. P. (1980). Some observations on the captive management of Galapagos tortoises. Reproductive Biology and Diseases of Captive Reptiles (ed. Murphy J. B. and Collins J. T). SSAR, USA.

Barten, S. L. (1982). Fatal metastic Mineralisation in a Red-footed tortoise. Veterinary Medicine, Small Animal Clinician. April 1982, 595-597.

Bellairs, A. (1969). The Life of Reptiles. Weidenfeld and Nicholson, London.

Cobo, M. and Andreu, A. (1988) Seed consumption and dispersal by the spur-thighed tortoise Testudo graeca. OIKOS 51:267-273.

Collins, D. (1971). Quantities of Calcium Carbonate needed to balance calcium-phosphorous ratios of various meats. Journal of Zoo Animal Medicine, Vol. 2, March 1971.

Dandifrosse, G. (1974). Chemical Zoology, Vol IX, Amphibia and Reptilia- Eds. Florkin, M. and Scheer, B. T. Academic Press, London and New York.

Dearden B. L, Hansen R. L, Steinhorst R. K. (1974). Analysis of the discernibility of plant species during digestion. Natural Resources Ecology Laboratory technical report 261, Colorado State Univ.

Engberg, N. J. (1980). Feeding your chelonian. Tortuga Gazette, April 1980.

Fenchel, T. M, McRoy C. P, Ogden J. C, Parker P. and Rainey W. E. (1979). Symbiotic cellulose degradation in Green Turtles. Applied and Environmental Microbiology 37 (2), p 348-355.

Finlayson, R. and Woods, S. J. (1977). Arterial Diseases Of Reptiles. Journal of the Zoological Society of London, 183. p 397-410.

Frye, F. L. (1974). The role of nutrition in the successful captive management of reptiles. Proceedings of the California Vet. Med. Association, 86th annual seminar p 5-15.

Hansen R. M, Johnson M. K., Van Devender T. R. (1976). Foods of the desert tortoise Gopherus agassizi in Arizona and Utah. Herpetologica 32, p 247-251.

Highfield, A. C. (1987). Causal factors of mortality in captive collections. Testudo Vol. 2 No 5, p 15-17.

Highfield, A. C. (1988). Practical Dietary Recommendations For Hatchling Tortoises. Tortoise Trust technical bulletin No 18.

Holt, P. E. (1978). Radiological studies of the alimentary tract in two Greek tortoises. Veterinary Record No. 103, p 198-200.

Jackson J. G, Trotter J. A, Trotter T.H, Trotter' M. W. (1976). Accelerated growth rate and early maturity in Gopherus agassizi Reptilia: Testudines. Herpetologica 32 p 139-145.

Kauffeld. C. (1969). The effect of altitude, ultra-violet light and humidity on captive reptiles. International Zoo Yearbook, Vol. 9, p 8-9,

Keymer, 1. F. (1978). Diseases of Chelonians: (1) Necropsy survey of tortoises. Veterinary Record, No. 103, p 542-548.

Lambert, M. R. K. (1986). On the Growth of the captive-bred Mediterranean Testudo in N. Europe. In Rocek, Z. (Ed.) Studies in Herpetology, 309-314. Prague: Charles University.

Lambert, M. R. K. (1988). Natural Bioclimatic range and the Growth of captive-bred Mediterranean Testudo L. in Northern Europe: Implications for conservation farming. British Herpetological Society Bulletin, No. 24, p 6-7.

Margen, S. (1974). Studies in calcium metabolism: 1. The calciuretic effect of dietary protein. American Journal of Clinical Nutrition, No. 27, p 584-589.

Reid, D. B. (1982). Feeding juvenile Tortoises. The Rephiberary, No. 61 p 1-2.

Reiter, R. J. and Follett, B.K- (Eds) (1980). Seasonal reproduction in higher vertebrates. Progress in Reproductive Biology, Vol: S. Karger, Basel.

Rosskopf, W. J. (1981). Initial findings in a three year mortality study on desert tortoises. Tortuga Gazette, May 1981, p 4-5.

Rosskopf, W. J. (1982). Severe shell deformity caused by a deficient diet in a California Desert Tortoise. Veterinary Medicine, Small Animal Clinician. April 1982, p 593-594.

Rosskopf, W. J. (1982). Normal hemogram and blood chemistry values for California desert tortoises. Tortuga Gazette, March 1982, p 4-6.

Samour H. J. Spratt D, Hart H. G, Savage B, Hawkey, C. M. (1987). Biomedical survey of the Aldabra Giant Tortoise *Geochelone gigantea* population on Curieuse island. Zoological Soc. of Lond-

Shaw, C. E. (1961). Breeding the Galapagos tortoise. International Zoo Yearbook, No. 3, p 102-104.

Skoczylas, R. (1978). Physiology of the Digestive Tract. In Gans, C. and Gans K. A. (Eds). Biology of the Reptilia, Vol. 8. Academic Press, London and New York.

Sokol, O.M. (1976). Herbivory of Lizards. Evolution, No 21, p 192-194.

Swingland, 1. R. (1984) Dietary preferences of free living chelonians. Symposium on Chelonian Nutrition and Malnutrition. Univ. of Bristol, summarized in The British Chelonia Group Newsletter, September 1984.

Tammar, A. R. (1974). In Chemical Zoology, IX, Amphibia and Reptilia- Eds. Florkin M, and Scheer B. T. Academic Press, London and New York.

Throp, J. L. (1979). Note on the management and reproduction of the Galapagos tortoise at Honolulu Zoo. In Martin R.D. (Ed.) Breeding Endangered Species in Captivity. Academic Press, London and New York.

Vivien-Roels B., Arendt J., and Bradtke J. (1979). Circadian and circannual fluctuations of pineal indoleamines (serotonin & melatonin) in Testudo hermanni- General and Comparative Endocrinology 37, 197-210.

Wallach, J. D. (1971). Environmental and nutritional diseases of captive reptiles. Journal of the American Veterinary Medical Association. No. 159, 1633-1643.

Wallach J. D. and Hoessele, C. (1966). Hypervitaminosis-D in Green Iguanas. Journal of the American Veterinary Medical Association. No. 149, 912-914.

Wallach J. D. and Hoessele, C. (1968). Fibrous osteodystrophy in Green Iguanas. Journal of the American Veterinary Medical Association. No. 153, 363-365.

Wagner, E. (1977). Some parameters for breeding reptiles in captivity. British Herpetological Society newsletter, No. 16, 8-21.

Will, R. (1975). Zentrablatt fur Veterinarmedizin. 22 : 617-626.

Zwart, P. and Van de Watering, C. (1969). Disturbance of bone formation in the Common Iguana (Iguana iguana L). Pathology and Biology. Acta Zoology and Pathology No. 46, 333-356.

Zwart, P. (1987). Advances in the veterinary care of chelonians over the past 20 years. Testudo Vol. 2 No. 5.

NOTES ON SKELETAL AND CARAPACE DEFORMITY IN CAPTIVE-BRED TORTOISES (GENUS;*TESTUDO*) RELATED TO DIET WITH OBSERVATIONS ON THE USE OF VITAMIN AND MINERAL SUPPLEMENTS

A. C. Highfield

(This paper was originally published by the International Herpetological Society)

Introduction

In a previous paper the author has described in some detail the dietary parameters necessary for normal healthy growth in herbivorous land tortoises and the effects of some dietary deficiencies and excesses (Highfield, 1988). The present paper examines two case histories which demonstrate severe osteological disorders resulting from a combination of excessive dietary protein and inadequate dietary calcium and suggests the use of extra-high Ca:P ratio dietary supplements.

Specimen background

1. *Testudo hermanni boettgeri* MOJSISOVICS 1889 (plate 1)

This tortoise was captive-bred by an amateur keeper and was 4 years old when presented to the author for examination. The carapace length was 122 mm and the weight 350g. Severe malformation of the vertebral region is evident, in combination with some 'pyramiding' of the scutes. The plastron was hard, but the carapace still exhibited an unusual degree of flexibility. There was additional evidence of locomotion difficulty concerning the back legs which were weak and carried at an unusual angle.

Plate 1 (above): Typical severe scute and spinal deformation due to feeding a high protein diet inadequate in calcium. Note carapace depression and position of hind limbs.
Plate 2 (below): Excessive keratin growth is evident in this specimen (see text).

The diet of this tortoise from hatching onwards had consisted of mainly of lettuce, tomato and small quantities of tinned cat food. Some calcium had been given as a supplement, but not consistently or according to any specific ratio. No multi-vitamin or mineral supplement containing D3 had been used, and exposure to natural daylight or artificial sources of U.V (e.g True-lite) had been minimal.

2. *Testudo ibera* PALLAS 1815 (plate 2)

This tortoise was 2 years old when examined. It weighed 545g and measured 150mm which is an abnormally large size for a tortoise of this species at such an age (compared to wild specimens). There was evidence of excessive keratin growth, not only of the scutes which were raised but also of the claws and beak. Both the plastron and the carapace were hard with no evidence of unusual flexibility. There were no locomotion difficulties.

The diet of this specimen was similar to that of the above with the addition of peas and beans plus a somewhat more varied vegetable intake. A multi-mineral and vitamin supplement had been used sparingly but regularly by the owner ('Vionate') and some extra calcium had also been given in the form of ground cuttlefish bone.

Analysis

Both specimens demonstrate symptoms characteristic of excessive consumption of dietary protein; e.g., accelerated growth and excessive growth of keratin resulting in a 'pyramid' formation of the scutes. In the former specimen there is additional evidence of severe osteodystrophy and osteoporosis resulting from the lack of D3 and a grossly inadequate Ca; P ratio. In the latter specimen the D3 and calcium content of the 'Vionate' appears to have prevented the situation deteriorating quite this far although osteological malformation is still evident. In addition, both specimens regularly excreted large concretions of solidified uric acid - a common phenomena in cases where excess dietary proteins are consumed by reptiles adapted for a low-protein diet.

Discussion

Both animals display classic symptoms of nutritional imbalance. The ideal ratio of calcium to phosphorous in herbivorous species is often quoted 2 : 1 for growing reptiles, at least 1.25 : 1 for fully grown adults, and 15 or even 20 : 1 in the case of carnivorous species. Calculations based upon the chemical constituents of wild tortoise diets suggest that an actual figure of 4 or even 8 parts Ca to 1 part P would be more realistic. 'Vionate' is an excellent general purpose supplement which contains many valuable trace elements and vitamins. It is not however sufficiently rich in calcium to counterbalance the high phosphate levels encountered in many green vegetables. Even where it is provided liberally it is very difficult to maintain a ratio of 1:1 or 2:1 in practice and virtually impossible to exceed these levels. Where meat or high protein vegetables such as beans are included in the diet 'Vionate' is totally inadequate to counter the reverse Ca:P ratio which is created. Any deficiency induced skeletal disorders will obviously manifest much more rapidly and with greater severity in an animal undergoing a rapid growth phase than in a fully grown adult.

Where the average mean protein content of the juveniles diet is maintained at circa 4% normal growth without excessive keratin production occurs. In our own program this is achieved by basing the diet on the following formula;

* 90% Green leaf plant material (including 'weeds')
* 10% Flower heads

No high protein vegetables, e.g., peas, beans or alfalfa are given and absolutely no meat products are included in the diet.

This diet is standard in our collection for *Testudo graeca, Testudo ibera, Testudo hermanni, Testudo marginata* and other members of the *Testudo* genus, including *T. kleinmanni*. A similar regime is adopted for Leopard tortoises (*Geochelone pardalis*), and Chaco tortoises (*Geochelone chilensis*).

This is supplemented daily with 'Nutrobal' (Vetark Animal Health)) a high potency calcium formulation containing additional vitamins and minerals including Vitamins-A, D3 (350ui/g), E, K, B1, B2, B6, B12 and C, with Manganese, Zinc, Selenium, Cobalt and Copper. The gross Ca:P ratio of the raw formulation is 46:1, and in practice this produces an estimated consumed ratio of circa 5:1 to 8:1 depending upon the existing Ca:P balance of the base. The 'Nutrobal' is applied at a rate of between 10g-25g per 500g of base diet depending upon the assessed requirements of the individual specimens.

The resulting hatchlings display entirely normal scute formation and carapace curvature and no evidence of osteological disturbance.

REFERENCE:

Highfield, A. C. (1988) Notes on dietary constituents for Herbivorous terrestrial chelonia and their effects on Growth and Development. ASRA (U.K) Journal, Vol.3 (3):7-20.

Principal Points

• Fast growth rates can be achieved by feeding high protein content diets, but with an increased risk of carapace deformity and renal disease. These problems may not manifest for several years in the case of adults, but usually manifest more rapidly in juveniles.
• Additional problems associated with high protein diets include articular gout, a condition which tends to reveal itself only after several years of incorrect feeding. No tortoise fed on a low protein (natural) diet has so far presented with this condition. By comparison, a large number of cases in tortoises which have been fed on high protein diets have been recorded.
• The success (or otherwise) of a diet can be determined only by studying the response of juveniles: adults have proved to be able to tolerate dietary mismanagement (excesses and deficiencies) for years before displaying symptoms. Long term damage does, however occur in adults. Dietary failures typically manifest in juveniles within 12-24 months: in adults it may take 5-10 years before the effects are seen.

TOXIC PLANT LIST

The following list is derived from multiple sources. Unfortunately, the degree of alleged toxicity is not known in many cases. Some plants are much more toxic than others. Some plants on this list may be safely consumed in moderate quantities, but may be toxic under certain circumstances or in large doses. Use this list as a general guide. Those plants which are especially dangerous to tortoises (cases where mortality has been reported following consumption) are clearly marked with an asterisk.

NB: Some plants appear more than once under alternative names.

Acokanthera
Aconite (monk's hood)*
Amaryllis
Amsinckia (tarweed)
Anemone
Apple (seeds only)
Apricot (seeds only)
Autumn crocus*
Avocado (leaves)
Azalea
Baneberry*
Beach pea
Betal nut palm*
Belladonna*
Bittersweet
Bird of paradise
Black locust
Bleeding heart
Bloodroot
Bluebonnet
Bottlebrush
Boxwood*
Buckeye horse chestnut
Buttercup
Caladium
Calla lily
Cardinal flower
Carolina jessamine
Casava
Castor bean
Chalice or trumpet vine
Cherry (seeds only)
Cherry laurel
China berry tree
Christmas berry
Christmas cactus (Euphorbia)
Christmas rose

Columbine
Common privet
Coral plant
Crocus*
Croton
Cyclamen
Daffodil*
Daphne
Death camus*
Deadly nightshade *
Delphinium
Destroying angel (death cap)*
Dogwood
Elderberry
Elephant ear (taro)
English ivy
Euphorbia
False hellebore
Fiddle neck (Senecio)
Fly agaric (amanita, deathcap)*
Four o'clock
Foxglove*
Gelsemium
Golden chain
Hemlock*
Henbane*
Holly
Horse chestnut
Horsetail reed (Equisetum)
Hyacinth
Hydrangea*
Impatiens
Iris
Ivy
Jack-in-the-pulpit
Jasmine
Jatropha

Jerusalem cherry
Jessamine
Jimson weed (thorn apple)*
Johnson grass, wilted
Lambkill (sheep laurel)*
Lantana camara
Larkspur
Laurel
Lily of the valley*
Lobelia
Locoweed*
Locust
Lupin*
Machineel
May apple
Mescal*
Milk weed
Mistletoe*
Moccasin flower
Monkshood*
Moonseed
Morning glory
Mountain laurel
Narcissus
Natal cherry
Nectarine (seed only)
Nicotine, tree, bush, flowering *
Nightshades*
Oak
Oleander*
Pear seeds
Pennyroyal
Peony*
Periwinkle
Philodendrons, some species
Pinks
Plum seeds
Poinsettia
Poison hemlock*
Poison ivy*
Poison oak*
Poison sumac*
Pokewood or pokeberry
Poppy (except California)
Potato (leaves)*
Privet
Redwood
Rhubarb (leaves)*
Rhododendron *
Rosemary

Russian thistle
Sage
Salmonberry
Scarlet pimpernel
Scotch broom
Senecio
Skunk cabbage
Snapdragon
Spanish bayonet
Squirrel corn
Sudan grass
Star of Bethlehem
Sundew
Sweetpea
Tansy
Taro (elephant ears)
Tarweed
Tiger lily
Toad flax
Tomato (leaves & plant)
Toyon berry
Tree of heaven
Trillium
Trumpet vine
Venus flytrap
Verbena
Virginia creeper
Water hemlock*
Wild parsnip
Wisteria
Yellow star thistle
Yew*

Some species do not exhibit toxic effects even after consuming plants that are highly toxic to mammals. Buttercups, for example, appear to be eaten by many pet tortoises over many years, without evident ill effect. On the other hand, just a few daffodil flowers have caused death in tortoises. This list is derived from toxicity data in mammals, and is conservative. Some plants that are toxic in mammals are less so in tortoises due to the very slow digestive processes of these animals. In other cases (as with American box turtles and some toxic fungi) there may be a natural immunity or resistance. As a general rule, it is best to exclude all plants that are definitely implicated in cases of poisoning.

15

VITAMINS, MINERALS AND SUPPLEMENTS

There is a great deal of misunderstanding concerning the role of vitamins and minerals Many people believe that the more you get of both the better - this is categorically not true, indeed, some vitamins and minerals can be positively dangerous if taken in excess. What is actually required is a balanced intake of essential vitamins and trace elements - not massive doses of individual vitamins in isolation which serve only to upset the balance and may cause relative deficiencies elsewhere.

It is also important to dispense with the myths, common among tortoise keepers, that vitamin deficiencies are the cause of a great deal of frequently encountered diseases or that a vitamin injection is necessary to assist with hibernation. Both claims are totally incorrect. In fact, genuine cases of primary vitamin deficiency (that it a deficiency caused by a lack of the vitamin in the diet rather than as a consequence of inability to metabolize the vitamin due to some other health problem) are quite rare. *In the last 15 or so years we have encountered maybe 5 or 6 cases of primary vitamin deficiency in tortoises.* In all of the cases we have seen, the base-line diet of the animals concerned was by any standards grossly inadequate and severely limited in range. There is virtually no chance of vitamin deficiencies occurring in tortoises which are fed on a well balanced, varied diet.

There are two common ways in which additional vitamins may be given:

Oral vitamin supplements
These are useful as a guarantee that all necessary vitamins are being supplied - but again, they are not essential if the base-line diet is of high quality and is sufficiently varied. Animals on natural browse do not need vitamin supplements although *mineral* supplements may well be necessary.

Vitamin injections
These should only be used to deliver specific vitamins in cases where a specific vitamin deficiency is known to exist. We are totally opposed to the routine use of vitamin injections - in most cases, they serve no useful purpose and indeed are a frequent cause of introduced infection via the injection site. Very few deficiencies are so acute that the much more effective and safer oral delivery route is not a satisfactory mode of treatment. Acute vitamin-A deficiencies may be dealt with by injection under veterinary direction, but few other cases require this kind of treatment. The use of a routine "vitamin booster" before or after hibernation is a complete waste of time and money. Furthermore, repeated unnecessary injections greatly increase the possibility of secondary infections and injection site abscessing.

VITAMINS vs. MINERALS

Many people are unclear as to the difference between vitamins and minerals, and especially about how the two interact (many minerals, calcium for example, depend upon the presence of certain vitamins, such as vitamin-D before they can be absorbed). Vitamins are organic substances which help regulate bodily functions. Acting as co-enzymes, vitamins aid the action of enzymes during the metabolism of dietary nutrients. There are about a dozen major vitamins, a deficiency of any one of which will result in a serious deficiency disease.

Vitamins are only required in relatively small quantities, but have a major effect upon the body's reproductive, digestive, nervous and muscular systems. Vitamins also affect tissue growth and anti-body production. Some important vitamins include:

VITAMIN-A
Important to the condition of the skin and mucous membranes, eye (especially retinal) condition, biochemical and reproductive functions. Plants contain beta-carotene which is converted to true vitamin-A in the body.

VITAMIN-B COMPLEX
The B-complex vitamins are water soluble and excesses are excreted in the urine. Vitamin B1, thiamine, is a regulator in the carbohydrate metabolism; Vitamin B2, riboflavin, is a co-enzyme in energy release and interacts with vitamin B6 and vitamin B12; Vitamin B3, niacin, is also crucial to the energy metabolism and is often obtained by converting the amino-acid tryptophan - this process requires the presence of thiamine, riboflavin and pyridoxine; Vitamin B6, pyridoxine, is involved in energy conversion from glycogen and in the synthesis of hemoglobin and antibodies; Vitamin B12 interacts with folic acid to govern the production of red blood cells. A deficiency causes pernicious anemia and neurological symptoms. This vitamin is only produced within the gastro-intestinal tract when various micro-organisms act upon trace level cobalt. Deficiencies can occur following malabsorbtion syndrome or as a consequence of severe parasite infestations. The B-complex is just that. A matrix of interacting and inter-dependant compounds.

VITAMIN-D
Sometimes called 'the sunshine vitamin', vitamin-D is a fat soluble vitamin which is essential to the absorption and utilization of calcium and phosphorous, as such, it plays a major role in bone formation. It can be obtained either naturally, by the action of ultra-violet light on sterols in the skin, or orally by supplementation - virtually all calcium/mineral supplements contain vitamin D in sufficient quantity. Note that vitamin-D is one of the most toxic of vitamins if consumed in excess, therefore, 'pure' vitamin-D oral supplements are potentially extremely hazardous and should only be used under qualified veterinary supervision. In a balanced formulation with calcium, no problems have been noted. Vitamin-D is best utilized by reptiles in the form of D3 rather than D2.

VITAMIN-C
Vitamin-C has many functions, but as it is present in almost all fruits and green vegetables, deficiencies are extremely unlikely in tortoises or other herbivorous reptiles.

VITAMIN-E
Vitamin E is a vital antioxidant. Acute deficiencies are most often seen in aquatic turtles which have been maintained on oily, fat-rich diets and may manifest as muscular dystrophy. The condition is rare in herbivorous reptiles. Therapy for clinically diagnosed cases should include a combination of Vitamin E and selenium, a trace element which is synergistic. Evidence obtained from other animals, especially birds, suggests that even marginal vitamin E deficiencies may result in reproductive problems and contribute to the non viability of eggs.

VITAMIN-K
A fat-soluble coagulation vitamin. This vitamin is synthesized in the gut by bacterial action and is also found in plant foods. It is especially abundant in green, leafy plants.

MINERALS

Minerals are quite different from vitamins and are both chemical regulators and construction materials - calcium forms a major part of a tortoise's body, more than any other mineral. Calcium deficiency is also extremely common as a growing tortoise requires substantial quantities of this mineral in order to build its skeleton. The building of healthy bone tissue is the result of many vitamins and minerals acting in co-operation with each other, however. Calcium is far from the only mineral element involved.

It is essential to note that calcium is poorly absorbed by the body whereas phosphorus is readily absorbed. It is very easy to feed a diet too concentrated in phosphorus because it is available in quantity in nearly every foodstuff whereas calcium occurs at much lower levels.

Calcium and phosphorus together account for three-fourths of the mineral elements in the body, and five other elements account for most of the rest. It is important to note that their actions are interrelated; no one mineral can function without affecting the others.

The major function of calcium is to act in co-operation with phosphorus to build and maintain bones. Calcium is also essential for healthy blood and also helps to regulate heartbeat. In addition, calcium assists in the process of blood clotting and helps prevent the accumulation of too much acid or too much alkali in the blood. In addition, it plays a part in muscle growth, muscle contraction (hence, it is especially important for females during egg laying) and nerve transmission. Calcium aids in the body's utilization of iron, helps activate several enzymes (catalysts important in metabolism), and helps regulate the passage of nutrients in and out of cell walls.

Calcium absorption is very inefficient. Two factors effect absorption directly; the availability of calcium in the diet and the current body need. Unabsorbed calcium is excreted. The amount absorbed depends largely on the type of calcium offered, for unless calcium is in the water soluble form (food) in the intestine, it will not be absorbed properly.

Certain substances interfere with the absorption of calcium (oxalic acids, for example, or excess protein consumption). When excessive amounts of fat combine with calcium, an insoluble compound is formed which cannot be absorbed.

PHOSPHORUS

Phosphorus is the second most abundant mineral in the body and is found in every cell. It often functions along with calcium. This balance of calcium and phosphorus is needed for these minerals to be effectively used by the body.

Phosphorus plays an important part in almost every chemical reaction within the body. It is important in the utilization of carbohydrates, fats and protein for growth, maintenance, and repair of cells and for the production of energy. It aids in the transference of heredity traits from parents to offspring. It is also necessary for proper skeletal growth, kidney function and transference of nerve impulses. Phosphorus absorption depends on the presence of vitamin D3 and calcium. If phosphorus content is high, additional calcium must be taken to maintain proper balance. There is no known toxicity of phosphorus. Phosphorus is available in abundance in a wide variety of foods, including practically all vegetable and animal-derived foods.

Miscellaneous trace elements
Calcium, phosphorus, potassium, magnesium, sodium, and sulfur are present in relatively high amounts in the body tissues. Other minerals are present in the most minute quantities but are essential for proper body functioning. Iron, copper, and fluorine are present in sufficient quantities from deep green leafy plants. Iodine is needed to maintain a positive calcium balance, so a multi-mineral mixture containing iodine should be provided in addition to supplementation of raw calcium. Cobalt is critical to the vitamin B12 metabolism in all grazing herbivores. Gut microflora manufacture fatty acids from ingested plant material and depend upon the presence of cobalt for this process. Deficiencies are well known in cattle and sheep. Symptoms of deficiency in these animals include anemia and repeated intestinal problems including scour and flagellates, etc. Zinc and selenium are also known to play an extremely important role in animal nutrition and reproduction and deficiencies of these are certainly a possibility in certain captive situations.

The role of supplements
It may be argued that where a 'natural' diet is provided no additional mineral or vitamin supplementation is required. The fundamental problem is a) defining exactly what the natural diet of a species is and b) the difficulty of providing it. Many species browse upon a very wide range of different plants, consuming leaves, flowers and frequently stems, roots, seeds and even soil particles in the process. The range of trace elements, proteins, oils, vitamins and other micronutritional elements thus made available is both complex and extensive. Many of these elements are also mutually interactive. Sunlight and hence UV-B exposure in the wild is also very different from that typically experienced in captivity.

While it may be entirely possible to avoid the use of supplements in a free-ranging situation within the natural bioclimatic range, achieving this under captive conditions is a very different matter. From the discussion of trace element requirements given above it will be noted that even marginal deficiencies may have serious consequences. For this reason, the routine use of a safe and effective multi-mineral and vitamin supplement is, in the author's opinion, by far the best and safest option.

Variability in commercial crops
There are some tortoise keepers who assert that it is relatively easy to compile a diet based upon store-purchased produce that can meet the calcium, other mineral trace-element, energy and vitamin demands of these animals. These optimistic individuals choose to rely upon published tables of mineral and other nutrient qualities of specific produce. What is usually not realized is that these tables are merely average figures, and actual content can vary wildly from these published figures. A whole host of factors can affect the calcium to phosphorus ratio of a common lettuce, for example: soil chemistry where grown, method of watering during growing, types and frequency of fertilizers used, season when grown, age of the plant at harvesting, to name but a few of these infinitely variable possibilities. Some lettuces are at the high end of the scale, others near the bottom.

Published tables give only averages based upon the actual sample tested. Lettuces grown in one field, under certain growing conditions, can differ markedly from the same variety of plant grown a mile down the road under different conditions. Further variations and deviations from published figures occur depending upon which part of the plant is analyzed. Outer leaves differ from inner leaves, for example. This is the case throughout the entire range of trace elements for which published figures are available. One sample may be quite rich in selenium and cobalt or calcium, another might be seriously deficient in terms of an tortoise's needs. These tables are only a very, very rough guide and should never be regarded as fully representative or reliable. Basing a diet upon these tables is a high risk enterprise indeed, and this is the main reason why the present author considers that sensible use of quality multi-mineral and calcium supplements is by far the safest and most reliable option to guarantee adequate intake. To give just a few measured examples, an orange may contain anything from 180 mg of vitamin C to none at all. 100 grams of carrot may contain from 70 to 18,500 iu of vitamin A....... 100 grams of lettuce from 0.1 to 16.9 mg of manganese... spinach, a supposedly good source of iron, from 0.1 to 158 mg per 100 grams. Relying upon published "average content" tables to constitute diets is therefore extremely unlikely to give any kind of real indication of what is actually being provided to your pet.

PRACTICAL GUIDELINES

- Try to ensure that all diets are as varied as possible - in this way, a wider cross-section of natural trace elements will be made available.
- Do not dose with 'pure' vitamins unless under veterinary direction - some pure vitamins, including vitamins A & D, are highly toxic if taken in excess. These should only be used as part of a treatment program to correct a properly diagnosed specific deficiency.
- Provide vitamins orally rather than by injection, where required, unless there are compelling veterinary reasons to the contrary.
- The regular use of a safe, properly formulated multi-vitamin and mineral preparation will ensure that dietary deficiencies do not occur.
- The best supplements for tortoises are phosphorus-free, contain a wide range of mineral trace elements, include vitamin-D3, and are free of added amino acids.
- If you maintain tortoises outdoors in a geographical zone where natural UV-B irradiation closely approximates that of the habitat in nature, then you many not need to provide additional oral D3 supplementation, though calcium and other trace elements should still be provided. Keepers in northern climes are generally advised to rely upon oral D3 supplements.
- Artificial UV-B lighting may be used, but tubes should be changed regularly (at least every 6-9 months) and multiple tube installations will be necessary to ensure adequate UV-B exposure for most species.
- Carnivorous turtles, and tortoises with a high degree of omnivory, will receive a significant proportion of their D3 needs from the animal protein proportion of their diet.
- Aim for a high calcium, low phosphorous content diet.
- Avoid plants high in oxalic or phytic acid.

	A COMPARISON BETWEEN NATURAL DIETS OF TROPICAL FOREST TORTOISES (*GEOCHELONE CARBONARIA* and *G. DENTICULATA*) AND THE DESERT TORTOISE (*GOPHERUS AGAZISSI*)	
	Red-Foot and Yellow-foot tortoise diet in Brazil *(after Moskovits and Bjorndal, 1990, Pritchard and Trebbau, 1984)*	**Desert tortoise diet in California** *(after Avery and Neibergs, 1997)*
Forage plants consumed, leaves, stalks, flowers:	Unidentified grasses, palm frond, vine stems, unidentified green leaves.	*Camissonia boothii, C. dentata, Cryptantha augustifolia, Malacothrix glabrata, Schismus barbata, Opuntia basilaris, Descurainia pinnata, Lepidium lasiocarpum*
Flowers only or stem and flowers only consumed:	*Jacaranda copaia, Cochlospermum orinocense, Mauritia flexuosa*	*Rafinesquia neomexicana, Stephanomeria exigua, Opuntia echinocarpa*
Fruits consumed:	*Spondias lutea, Anacardium gigantea, Philodendron sp., Bromiliad sp., Passiflora coccinea, P. verspertillo, Mauritia flexuosa, Duguetia surinamensis, Genipa americana, Pradosia sp., Clavija sp., Ficus sp., Annona Sp.*	None.
Seeds consumed:	Unknown.	*Pectocarya platycarpa, P. recurvata.*
Carrion consumed:	Agouti, peccary, bird, snake, lizard, and deer carcasses.	None.
Live prey consumed:	Snails, ants, termites, bees, beetles, butterflies.	None.
Miscellaneous items:	Mushrooms (several species), sand, soil, pebbles, tortoise feces, bark.	Soil, cattle feces.

Wild Foods for Tortoises

The following list is largely derived from observations of tortoises feeding in the wild (mainly Greece and Turkey) by Lin King. It also includes plants favored by tortoises which grow in Britain (many Mediterranean plants also grow here; in other cases close relatives grow here).

It is strongly advised that these plants form the basis of a high fiber staple diet for herbivorous tortoises. In all cases, we recommend the regular addition of a quality multi-mineral and vitamin supplement which includes trace elements such as zinc and selenium. It cannot be emphasized too strongly that requirements will vary from one species to another : in general, those animals which are found in drier areas such as around the Mediterranean tend to have a lower need for trace elements because they have adapted to the shortage of such elements in their native habitats.

If you are able to grow a selection of these plants yourself, you should consider the soil type in your garden. The soil type has a major impact upon the availability of minerals and hence on the composition of plants grown upon it. On **acid** soils, small annual applications of a mineral dressing such as calcified seaweed, which can supply calcium, magnesium and trace elements to the pasture, will help to ensure that animals receive adequate intakes. If you apply the dressing to only part of your plot, you will be able to see whether your animals choose to crop the treated or untreated areas.

If, on the other hand, your soils are already **lime** (calcium) rich, then a seaweed meal dressing will help to boost the trace element content of these soils which tend to be deficient.

Be careful to avoid picking plants from areas contaminated by lead (from vehicle exhausts) or from areas which may have been subjected to chemical spraying.

Recommended basic food plants:

- Dandelion (*Taraxacum officianale*)
- Hawkbits (*Leontodon spp.*)
- Sowthistles (*Sonchus spp.*)
- Hawkweeds (*Pictis spp.*)
- Hawkbeards (*Crepis spp.*)
- Plantains (*Plantago spp.*)
- Clovers (*Trifolium spp.*)
- Honeysuckle (*Lonicera periclymenum*) [preferred by *T. hermanni*]
- Cat's ears (*Hypochoeris spp.*)
- Vetches (*Vicina spp.*)
- Trefoils (*Lotus spp.*)
- Mallows (*Malva spp.*)
- Bindweeds (*Calystegia spp.*)
- Sedums (*Sedum spp.*)
- Ivy-leaved Toadflax (*Cymbalaria muralis*)

Also (observed eaten by *T. hermanni* and *T. marginata* in Greece):

- Robinia (pseudo-acacia) leaves
- Wild clematis
- Acanthus
- Nettles

In practice, the important thing is to provide a variety of fresh 'natural' graze. This is vastly superior to 'supermarket salads' and will supply a far greater range of minerals and essential trace elements. The fiber content will also be far high than 'commercial' salads. If you can manage to grow some of these plants in your tortoise enclosure your tortoises will certainly appreciate your efforts. Not only Mediterranean tortoises will benefit from a healthier diet. Ashley Woods, a Tortoise Trust member who keeps and breeds leopard tortoises (*Geochelone pardalis*), includes several wild plants in their daily diet. "This is a summary of a diet regime adopted by myself for a breeding colony of *Geochelone pardalis babcocki* held in my collection, it is also used with success for other species including all *Testudo* species and *Geochelone sulcata* (African spurred tortoise). Many suggested captive diets are all too low in one factor - fiber. Leopard tortoises must have a high fiber intake. During spring, summer and early Autumn all my tortoises are fed a diet of 85% wild greens and flowers, commercial greens and fruits are offered as a treat, usually on a once weekly basis. Wild food is not only high in fiber but also has the correct calcium/phosphorus ratio. When collecting wild foods take care of pesticides, try to be familiar with your local area and have 'safe' places for collecting. Also try to leave the roots intact so the plant can recover and grow again.

A list of wild food offered:

Please note this list is in addition to a large free range area where animals can graze and browse on various grasses and clovers - grass is a very important factor in the diet of leopard tortoises.

- Dandelion   *(Taraxacum officinale)* leaves, stems and flowers.
- Red clover   *(Trifolium pratence)* leaves, stems & flowers
- White clover   *(Trifolium repens)* leaves, stems and flowers.
- Greater Plantain *(Plantago media)*
- Ribgrass or Ribwart Plantian *(Plantago lancealata)*
- Smooth Sow Thistle *(Sonchus oleraceus)* leaves, stems & flowers
- Prickly Sow Thistle *(Sonchus asper)* coarsely or finely chopped.
- White-Dead Nettle * *(Lamilim album)*
- Red-Dead Nettle *(Lamium pupureum)*
- Chickweed * *(Stelaria media)*
- Smooth hawks-beard *(Crepis capilloris)* leaves & flower
- Hedge mustard *(Sisymbrium offlcinale)* young plants
- Bramble (*Rubus fruticosus*) shoots, tender leaves & fruit.

Weeds marked * flower and grow throughout the year and can be collected during winter (except in very cold frosty spells) making them a useful addition to winter diets. Obtain a wild plant book and cross reference Latin to common names as some common names may differ regionally.

The above greens and flowers are offered daily throughout spring and summer, and these are supplemented with Vionate for adults or Nutrobal or Rep-Cal with D3 for juveniles and breeding females. If you live in Arizona, or southern California, or other region with natural tortoise populations, and your tortoises spend most of the year out of doors, in natural, unfiltered sunlight you may not need to add pre-formed vitamin D3 via the diet. You should continue to add raw phosphorus-free calcium, however, preferably in the form of food grade calcium carbonate.

GRASSES AND HAYS FOR LEOPARD AND SULCATA TORTOISES

For large savannah species, such as *Geochelone sulcata* (African spurred tortoise) or *Geochelone pardalis* (Leopard tortoise), grasses and hays are a critical dietary component. Aldabra and Galapagos tortoises also do extremely well on this type of diet. Some other species also benefit from the inclusion of both fresh and dried grasses in their diet - although certain species, such as Red-foot, Yellow-foot, Hinge-back and Mediterranean tortoises are ill-equipped to digest the high silica content of grass fodder. For species adapted to it, however, grass is not only nutritious, but its fiber content makes a significant contribution to digestive health. For leopard and African spurred tortoises, mixed grasses should comprise approximately 70-75% of the total diet.

Availability of grass types varies greatly according to location. The following list of suitable fodder grasses is based upon availability in the USA. In Europe, these particular species are rarely available - although local equivalents can usually be found. General "meadow hay" and "orchard hay" mixes are usually suitable, for example. Avoid hays that have excessively "prickly" seed heads - these can injure mouths or eyes. The use of coarse Timothy hay is excluded on this basis. Second or third cuttings of grass hays tend to have less spiny heads than first cuttings.

- Buffalo grass
- Couch grass
- Kikuyu grass
- Dallas grass
- Blue Grama grass
- Big Bluestem grass
- Darnel Rye grass
- Wintergrass or Bluegrass
- Western Wheatgrass
- *Fescue* sp. grasses

This grass-based primary diet should be supplemented with flowers as frequently as possible (Hibiscus, dandelion, petunia, *Viola* sp. etc.,). De-spined *Opuntia* pads and fruit, clovers and other fodder 'weeds' listed previously should also be included on a regular basis.

Top to bottom, from left:

1. Desert tortoise juvenile demonstrating abnormal growth following vivarium rearing and high food availability.
2. More natural, smooth growth based on lower food intake and outdoor rearing.
3. *Geochelone carbonaria*, a highly omnivorous tropical species with high fruit intakes.
4. Perfect development in this captive-bred *T. g. graeca* based on low protein foods and slow growth at the Tortoise Trust.
5. A healthy captive diet for *Testudo* species as offered at the Tortoise Trust.
6. Shell deformity in a Chaco tortoise raised on canned dog food....

Top to bottom, from left:

1. Normal, healthy growth in an African Spurred tortoise, *Geochelone sulcata*.

2. Same species demonstrating 'pyramiding' due to dietary mismanagement (high protein and over-feeding).

3. *Opuntia* cacti are an excellent food for herbivorous tortoises; low in protein, high in fiber and rich in miscellaneous trace elements, including calcium.

4. Normal development in a Radiated tortoise, *Geochelone radiata*. This animal was reared on a diet based on *Opuntia* and similar low protein, high fiber, high mineral content plants.

5. By contrast, this badly deformed *G. radiata* was raised on a diet that included high protein foods. Note the darkened, thickened keratin in addition to the obvious 'pyramiding'.

Top to bottom, from left:

1. *Geochelone elegans.* The Indian Star tortoise. Normal development.
2. Same species, deformed carapace following rearing on high protein diet including frozen peas.
3. American box turtle - a genuinely omnivorous species.
4. A wild tortoise in Tunisia browses on leaves, flowers and stalks in the lush spring vegetation.
5. By mid-summer, this Tunisian tortoise estivates, buried in sand, to escape the extreme heat and to conserve energy during food shortages.

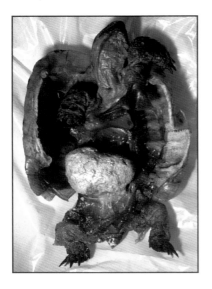

Top to bottom, from left:

1. The huge bladder stone that killed this juvenile *T. ibera* resulted from a diet based upon peas, beans and dog-food.
2. Discarded snail-shells litter the desert in Egypt and are actively sought out by tortoises as a useful source of calcium.
3. *Gopherus* habitat in Arizona. Like most arid habitat tortoises, *Gopherus* are strict herbivores.
4. This *T. graeca graeca* crops new vegetation following seasonal rains.
5. Tropical tortoise habitat. In habitat like this in Africa, *Kinixys homeana* and *K. erosa* are found. A plentiful supply of invertebrates and fresh water permit a relatively high protein diet compared to arid habitat species.

Feeding aquatic turtles

The diet of most turtles is, by contrast to land tortoises, heavily dependent upon animal protein (though see note on how this changes with age, below). Aquatic turtles are predators and opportunistic omnivores consuming a wide range of small fish, snails and similar creatures. These provide not only protein but also calcium in balanced amounts (whole animals are eaten - bones included - not just the fleshy parts). In captivity, it is essential not to make the all-too-common mistake of feeding only the `best' meat minus the calcium containing bones. Large bone splinters can, however, prove to be a danger in their own right if swallowed whole so many keepers prefer to provide calcium in a safer form (usually as a proprietary supplement). Good quality supplements of proven performance include 'Rep-Cal' and 'Miner-All' with D3 (US availability) and 'Nutrobal' (European availability).

Most turtles are actually omnivorous rather than exclusively carnivorous, consuming both animal prey and plant material in the wild. Slider and Painted turtles tend to be far more carnivorous as juveniles, than as adults. **It is very easy to overfeed adults on protein-rich meat-based products - do not forget that in the wild adults of many common species are predominantly herbivorous!**

In all cases, it is certainly not adequate to feed only on commercial turtle flakes which are often of very poor nutritional value and severely lacking in dietary fiber, vitamins and minerals. Nor should oily fish form the staple diet, as these can result in steatitis or fatty infiltration of the liver. Diets containing excessive quantities of fish can also result in induced vitamin-B deficiencies due to the presence in fish of an enzyme called thiaminase, which interferes with the take up of B-group vitamins. **It should also be noted that fish oils and fresh meat waste in the water is extremely slow to degrade - it can clog filters and quickly result in bad smelling, poor water quality.**

The main thing to avoid with diets for any captive turtle is over-reliance upon one single item; this is a very easy mistake to make, but a balanced and varied diet is infinitely superior. Provide as wide a range of the following food items as you possibly can.

Suggested turtle diet

- Plant leaf, aquatic plant and salad material, assorted (freely available)
- Raw (whole) small fish (not frozen, very limited amounts occasionally)**
- Rehydrated low fat dried cat, dog and trout pellets (twice weekly for juveniles - no more than once weekly for adults)
- Zoophobas, crickets and waxworm larvae (limited amounts, occasionally)***
- Earthworms (occasionally)
- Tubifex and bloodworms (excellent for tempting hatchlings to begin feeding)
- Small snails and mollusks (occasionally)**
- Good quality proprietary foods (e.g., Reptomin®) three times per week

*** Note that these items carry some risk of transmission of certain parasitic organisms such as flukes. For this reason, you may care to exclude them. Turtles can be reared perfectly satisfactorily if these items are omitted.*

*** These are particularly useful if confronted by a rescued wild turtle that may not immediately recognize prepared foods as edible.*

An average meal can consist of two or three of the above constituents, combined. Rotate ingredients for variety and balance. **We have maintained, bred and reared quite literally hundreds of turtles over the past 20 years using this as our general, base-line diet.**

Where dried food, or floating food sticks, are to be rehydrated, it is better to rehydrate using water *plus* a calcium and vitamin additive. Live prey and salad vegetation should also be dusted in this manner immediately prior to feeding. This is a highly successful way of ensuring that your turtle will obtain all of the essential vitamins and trace elements it requires. **On no account rely upon 'Turtle Flakes', dried shrimp, or 'ant eggs' as sold in some stores - these products are totally unsuited to the successful rearing of healthy turtles.** Most turtles fed on such diets die within a few months from multiple dietary deficiencies.

To avoid contaminating your turtles with Salmonella organisms, it is wise not to feed raw meats, especially chicken or pork - these frequently harbor the organism and if eaten by the turtle the disease will be passed on. *Diets rich in meats are invariably also high in phosphorus and low in calcium.* This can cause serious problems for turtles, who need high levels of calcium for healthy bone and carapace development. Note that in the wild most aquatic turtles feed regularly upon snails and similar creatures which have a calcium-rich shell. Insect larvae, as taken in considerable numbers by juvenile turtles in the wild, are also comparatively rich in calcium. In captivity, this source is rarely available and therefore additional calcium supplementation is absolutely essential. Calcium tablets can be successfully hidden in meats, and all foods should heavily dusted with a general high ratio calcium-mineral supplement such as Rep-Cal, Miner-All, etc. Provision of a cuttlefish bone which can be gnawed if required is also recommended. The 'Calcium Blocks' sometimes sold for turtles are not adequate by themselves and should not be relied upon to prevent Metabolic Bone Disease (MBD) - always use a professional grade reptile supplement containing a balanced quantity of food-grade, phosphorus-free calcium with vitamin D3.

In turtles with MBD, the bones of the jaw may be soft and weak and in hatchlings the plastron may remain soft long after it ought to have hardened. Nervous symptoms associated with hypocalcaemia may also be noted (shaking, tremors). These symptoms may appear collectively or individually depending upon the progression and severity of the deficiency. Hatchlings are worse affected (due to their rapid growth and consequent higher calcium demand) but even adults will manifest the condition if placed on an acutely deficient or severely unbalanced diet for long enough.

The underlying bony tissue is porous and thickened and local swellings of the jaw and limbs are commonplace. The body, attempting to support the weakened skeleton, surrounds it with a fibrous connective tissue. The parathyroid glands recognize that there is inadequate calcium within the blood-stream, and attempt to rectify the deficiency by leaching calcium from the bones, thus exacerbating the condition. As long as the diet and blood-serum level remain calcium deficient, this vicious cycle continues. Finally death occurs from acute 'calcium collapse'. This condition results directly from inadequate levels of dietary calcium, excessive dietary protein, excessive dietary phosphorous and inadequate levels of vitamin D3. Generally a combination of factors are involved. **The condition is 100% preventable and the use of a balanced diet, regular use of quality supplement and provision of UV-B lighting will ensure that it does not affect your turtle.**

Feeding quantity and frequency

Finally on the topic of feeding, it is definitely the case in my experience that over-rather than under-feeding tends to be the main problem in many captive situations; in the long term this can prove just as damaging as underfeeding. Not only must the quality of the diet be maintained within safe limits, but the quantity too. This applies equally to land tortoises and aquatic turtles; in the latter case if you overfeed you will not only get fatty, obese and lethargic turtles but you will also very quickly experience serious tank hygiene problems - and an almost certain outcome of that will be a dramatic increase in the incidence of infectious disease. In most cases, feeding 3-4 times per week will be quite adequate. Daily feeding is hardly ever required with aquatic turtles - although unrestricted access to aquatic vegetation such as water hyacinth will do no harm.

In the wild, this changeover from a diet rich in animal content, to one of predominately aquatic vegetation, occurs at a carapace length of approximately 1.75 to 2.75" (4 cm to 6 cm). During the heavily carnivorous phase, the diet consists of 85% insect matter and 15% plant material. In the case of adults, and almost complete reversal occurs, with 90% plant matter and less than 10% from animal sources.

It is also worth noting that fresh meats and fish are particularly troublesome in respect of tank hygiene - where these items are given, I would strongly recommend feeding in a separate container to avoid contaminating the main tank and overloading the filters. Dried, rehydrated foods cause few such problems by comparison and are much better suited to routine, in-tank feeding. If you find you are having to remove uneaten food from the tank, you are either *a)* overfeeding *b)* have the maintenance temperature too low which is discouraging normal feeding or *c)* have a sick turtle.

Feeding box & wood turtles

These North American semi-terrestrial turtles are omnivorous in their feeding habits. In the wild, they consume slugs, snails, earthworms and similar small prey as well as fallen fruits, mushrooms and some green leaf material. Juvenile box turtles are often almost exclusively carnivorous, their diet broadening out to include more vegetable matter with increasing age.

Suggested diet for box & wood turtles

- Slugs, snails
- Earthworms, waxworm larvae, mealworms, night crawlers
- Beetles
- Fruit (most turtles prefer "mushy" over-ripe fruits rather than fresh)
- Green leaf vegetables
- Mushrooms
- Small quantity (low fat) dog food, thawed pinkie mice (for *T. ornata*)

As with all tortoises and turtles, great care must be taken to ensure a varied diet adequate in all essential trace elements. Regular supplementation of the diet with a vitamin-mineral powder is therefore recommended - calcium supplementation during their carnivorous phase is especially critical.

Feeding tropical tortoises

The term 'tropical tortoise' covers a very diverse range of animals, from even more varied habitats. From tortoises which live in semi-arid desert such as *Geochelone sulcata* (African Spurred tortoise), to tortoises of the grassy savannahs such as *Geochelone pardalis* (Leopard tortoise), through rain-forest animals such as *Geochelone denticulata* (Yellow-foot tortoise) and some (not all) members of the *Kinixys* (Hinge-back) group.

From the above it will be clear that no single diet can be recommended as suitable for such a wide range of tortoises with such different preferences and requirements. However, it is possible to make a few general recommendations based upon our own and our members' experience of keeping all of the above mentioned species. Firstly, most tropical species' diets can be broadly categorized as either;

Entirely herbivorous
or
Omnivorous

There are no *entirely* carnivorous land tortoises. From this, it follows that for practical purposes, all tropical tortoise diets can be accommodated by combining elements from the suggestions for herbivorous land tortoises such as *T. graeca* or *T. hermanni* or for semi-carnivorous aquatic chelonia such as terrapins or box turtles. The problem for keepers is to know which diet suits which particular tortoise. The following guide-lines provide a useful starting point based upon our personal experience:

Red-foot and Yellow-foot tortoises; Bell's, Eroded & Home's Hinge-back tortoises

These tortoises are basically omnivorous or a greater or lesser extent. Precise tastes vary. A recent study of wild Yellow-foot and Red-foot tortoises revealed some interesting data; this is compared to the typical diets of the Desert tortoise in the table on page 21. Include some low-fat animal protein in the diet of these species. Protein (or more probably, an amino-acid) deficiency has been noted in some Red-foot and Yellow-foot tortoises raised on *entirely* herbivorous diets. We recommend re-hydrating dried cat foots with additional minerals and vitamins as for turtles. Provide one meal per week containing animal protein. We now give about 25g of moist cat food to a fully grown Red-foot tortoise on a weekly basis (proportionally less for juveniles). Fruits are also part of the diet of these species in the wild - unlike Leopard or African spurred tortoises, their digestive tract copes easily with this richer, sweeter intake. The same frequency seems to suit Hinge-backs, which are also highly omnivorous in nature, but here approximately 5-10 g of animal protein per week is more appropriate (depending upon size). It is also important to note that these tortoises, if allowed access to a damp, moist garden or well vegetated tropical house will usually find slug, snails and night crawlers for themselves. This is both psychologically and gastronomically stimulating for them in addition to helping out with their owners' garden pest control efforts! Needless to say, **never use slug pellets or other toxic chemicals** in any garden where tortoises (of any sort) are kept. Millipedes and similar invertebrates constitute an important part of the diet of *Kinixys* sp. in nature.

ANTI-NUTRIENT FACTORS IN COMMON TORTOISE DIETS

Although the potential for oxalic acid to inhibit calcium uptake from plants has been known for some time, this is by no means the only potentially problematic chemical in plant foods that should be of concern to keepers of herbivorous reptiles. Phytic acid is another compound that can seriously disrupt mineral uptakes. This brief review summarizes specific plant compounds that are of concern, and lists foods that contain them in significant amounts. Items that give rise to special concern are those that contain multiple anti-nutrient factors at relatively high levels. These are clearly marked with asterisks in the tables that follow, and there would seem to be strong reasons for excluding these completely from the diet of any captive herbivorous animal. Items that appear under several anti-nutrient headings should not feature as regular dietary constituents, or be fed at high volumes even intermittently.

Oxalic acid

Oxalic acid occurs naturally in many plants. At very high doses it can be rapidly fatal, causing ulceration, convulsions and vomiting. Few plants with domestic availability fall into this class, for obvious reasons; rhubarb leaves and uncooked stems are a rare exception. Oxalic acid binds with calcium, iron, magnesium, sodium and potassium to form less soluble salts known as oxalates. Renal calculi (stones) formed of calcium oxalate are relatively common. In addition, the presence of high levels of dietary oxalic acid in plants seriously inhibits the availability of any calcium they may contain (as little as 5% of the calcium in spinach is available for this reason). Low levels of oxalic acid intake are not harmful - but high levels are implicated in the etiology of kidney stones and therefore should be discouraged. Plants that contain high levels of oxalic acid (generally accepted as being over 200 parts per million) include:

Beans* (average 300 ppm), bell peppers, rhubarb* (average 12,000 ppm), spinach*, strawberries, beets, buckwheat (111,000 ppm), beet greens*, lambsquarter (*Chenopodium album* - at 300,000 ppm exceptionally high) cranberries, summer squash, sweet potatoes, soy beans, tofu*, Swiss chard*, celery, eggplant/aubergine, nasturtium, corn, star fruit (50,000 - 95,000 ppm), garden sorrel (3,000 ppm), mango (300 ppm), banana* (5,240 ppm) pumpkin, purslane (*Portulaca oleoracea* - 16,750 ppm), cauliflower*, and cabbage* (average 350 ppm) and mustard greens* (high at 1,300 ppm).

Phytic acid

Phytic acid is found in most cereal grains, legumes, nuts, oilseeds, tubers and organic soils. Phytic acid accounts for up to 85% of the total phosphorus in cereals and beans. The concentration of phytic acid in foods ranges from 0.4% to 10.7% by weight. The primary anti-nutrient property of phytic acid is that it binds with minerals and proteins, inhibiting their uptake and utilization. In this respect, it closely parallels oxalic acid. The ability of phytic acid to bind with starch (carbohydrate) has also been demonstrated. Of the mineral trace elements, zinc is most profoundly affected by high levels of phytic acid consumption, although calcium, magnesium, manganese, and iron are also affected to lesser extents. The foods highest in phytic acid include peas and beans (1-4%) wheat bran (5%), rice bran (8%), and soy concentrate (10.7%). Attempts to compensate by over-supplementing diets high in phytic acid with additional calcium are counter-productive, as this exaggerates the inhibition of zinc uptake producing a very real danger of deficiency. It is best to avoid feeding excessive quantities of phytic acid rich foods from the outset. Foods contra-indicated by their high phytic acid content include:

Peas* (average 10,000 ppm), beans* (average 4,800 ppm), Swiss chard*, rhubarb*, brown rice, okra, parsley, beet greens*, collard greens*, wheat (48,500 ppm), soya meal/beans*, millet*, oats, rye, pumpkin seed (22,000 ppm) buckwheat*, and corn*. Most bread, especially wholemeal bread, is also very rich in phytic acid.

Glucosinolates/Goitrogens

These compounds, found at particularly high levels within the cabbage family, decrease the absorption of iodine by the thyroid gland, limiting the formation of iodine-containing precursors of thyroxine, the production of which is decreased. This results in a reactionary enlargement of the thyroid, or goiter Simply supplementing with additional iodine can help, but is not a complete answer as the mechanism is different from that found in goiter resulting from a primary deficiency of dietary iodine. Limiting consumption of vegetables containing high levels of goitrogenic compounds is therefore recommended:

Bok-choi, Brussels sprouts, kale, radish ,broccoli, cabbage*, rutabaga, black mustard, cauliflower*, horseradish, kohlrabi, meadowfoam, rutabaga, stinkweed, millet, soya beans*, turnip greens* and watercress.

Purines

Purines were first discovered in uric acid in the 19th Century. Even then, it was clear that there was a strong link between these compounds and gout in humans. Purines are employed by the body in a constructive mode to rid cells of excess nitrogen, as anti-oxidants, as chemical messengers, and as energy transducers. High purine intakes do, however, have serious consequences. Some people are highly susceptible to these compounds and there are several genetic disorders of the purine metabolism. Purines are of special concern to reptile keepers because of their very close connection with uric acid. High levels of purine intake directly increase uric acid generation. This in turn places additional demands upon the renal system. Kidney diseases are one of the most common causes of death among captive herbivorous reptiles. Foods that are extremely high in purines include:

All beans*, peas*, pulses and legumes, asparagus, avocados, mushrooms, spinach*, cauliflower*, all soya meals*, tofu, all meat products, sardines, anchovies, herring, mackerel, shrimp, tuna, salmon

Note: High purine foods can be safely consumed by most carnivorous aquatic species, and by many semi-terrestrial or terrestrial humid habitat species. They are most damaging to semi-arid habitat species, animals with pre-existing renal problems, or those suffering from dehydration. Where high purine foods are used it is absolutely critical that a source of fresh water should be available at all times.

Tannins
Consumption of vegetation containing high levels of tannins (plant polyphenols) can have a seriously inhibiting effect upon protein and starch availability of other vegetation consumed simultaneously, as it binds with proteins within the gut, protecting them from effective microbial digestion or fermentation. This is known to occur as tannin levels reach 2-4%. At levels of 5% and beyond, further adverse effects are observed, including inhibition of fiber digestion. At levels of 9% and above, consumption can prove rapidly fatal. Low levels of tannins are generally beneficial - it is only when consumed at high concentrations that it is considered an anti-nutrient, or as dangerous. Plants that contain levels of tannins that would give rise to such concerns if consumed in quantity include:

Black and red beans*, kiwi fruit, pomegranate (17,000 ppm), walnuts (147,000 ppm), alfalfa (27,000 ppm), chicory, oak and acacia leaves, bananas*, carrots and carrot tops, rhubarb*, spinach*

* Items that include several different anti-nutrient factors. It is recommended that these items be excluded from regular use.

CURING DIETARY ADDICTION

In more than 20 years of advising people about tortoise and turtle diets, the Tortoise Trust has encountered some terrible examples of dietary mismanagement - usually with tragic consequences for the unfortunate animal concerned. Some of the worst diets we have ever encountered include:

- The Red-eared slider fed only on ham and chocolate
- The *G. sulcata* raised on bagels and cream cheese
- The Mediterranean tortoise given bread, milk and cheese
- The Red-foot tortoises offered only canned cat food
- The American box turtle fed on ice-cream and apple pie
- The Marginated tortoise reared on peas, beans and dog food

Tortoises and turtles do not know what is good or bad, and tend to have very 'addictive' feeding behavior once introduced to a particular artificial diet. There is no excuse for offering items such as bread, milk, cheese, peas, beans, ice-cream, or canned cat and dog food to herbivorous tortoises. Even omnivorous and carnivorous species require sound dietary management. Should you encounter an animal reared on diets as listed above, you should cease offering the offending constituents immediately and re-adjust the diet to meet conventional and appropriate standards. Some animals will resist the change to a safe and nutritious diet. Simply continue offering appropriate foods and on no account revert to these "killer" ingredients. Ensure adequate hydration, but otherwise leave them to feed when they become sufficiently hungry. Most animals reared on the appalling diets described above are, in any event, obese and suffering from a fatty liver. Some weight loss is usually beneficial. Monitor their progress carefully, under qualified veterinary direction. Sometimes drug therapy is required to deal with the consequences of excess saturated fat consumption so typical of these diets. Eventually, if offered appropriate foods and maintained under the correct environmental conditions, the majority of animals will eventually revert to a healthy feeding pattern.

Further Insights into the Nutritional Requirements and Disorders of Tortoises; Protein, Energy, and Environment

A. C. Highfield

The link between protein intake and rapid rates of growth in tortoises and turtles is well-established (Jackson, Trotter, 1976, Avery, 1989). In this respect, tortoises are no different from other herbivorous reptiles where growth rates and age of sexual maturity are also strongly influenced by dietary considerations (Bjorndal, 1985, 1987, King, 1996, McArthur, 1996, Van Devender, 1982, Harris, 1982, Iverson, J.B. 1982) or indeed, from the majority of other animals, including mammals (Robbins, 1983). In tortoises raised on high protein, high growth rate regimes, it has long been observed that certain carapace deformities are commonplace (Highfield, 1988, Lambert, M. R. K. 1986, Rosskopf, W. J., 1982, Wallach, J. D. 1971, Jackson and Fasal, 1981). Conversely, the adoption of a low protein, high fiber, high calcium content diet and the avoidance of overfeeding has been conclusively demonstrated to reduce or prevent the condition (Highfield, 1990, 1996, 1999). The weight of this evidence has not prevented alternative hypotheses being regularly proposed. Solar (1997) suggested that dietary intake of pre-formed vitamin D3 was primarily responsible for 'pyramiding' or 'lumpy shell syndrome'. The methodology and conclusions drawn were seriously open to question, however (Highfield, 1997). Latterly, it has been suggested that environment exerts a greater influence upon the formation of these shell disorders than does nutrition, or the use of a high protein diet (Fife, R., 2000). This brief review of the relevant biology is presented in order to describe the mechanisms involved in the formation of "pyramided" or "lumpy shell syndrome" carapaces, and to explain precisely what the role of environment and dietary specialization is in this process. Also addressed is the issue of the differing levels and types of carbohydrates required by savannah and rain forest species.

Classes of carapace deformity linked to diet

Carapace deformities fall into two broad classes. The first class is that observed in animals that have been reared on an all-round deficient diet; deficient in calcium, vitamins, trace elements and other essential nutrients. A typical example would be a tortoise reared on a lettuce, tomato and cucumber diet without mineral supplementation. Such animals typically manifest with classical "softshell syndrome", where the bones of the plastron and carapace remain pliable long after they would normally have hardened. Some degree of "pyramiding" or "lumpiness" is present, but typically not to a gross degree. The pelvic area of the carapace is typically depressed, and there may be concurrent problems with feeding due to the bones of the jaw being similarly affected (Cooper and Jackson, 1981, Mader, 1996, Wallach, 1971). On dissection, the bony tissue is fibrous, porous, fractures easily and is many times thicker than normal (Highfield, 1990). Keratin thickness is normal, however and abnormal urea levels are atypical. Serum urea levels, if anything, tend to be at the lower end of normal deviation. Growth rates are not artificially accelerated, but rather tend to be inhibited (Highfield, unpublished data). The etiology of this class of deformity is identical to that seen in all other animals where calcium deficient diets are provided (Robbins, 1983) and in green iguanas and other herbivorous lizards raised on similarly calcium and or vitamin D3 deficient dietary regimes (Donoghue, S. in Mader, 1996). The problem can be prevented by providing adequate levels of dietary calcium, by ensuring that the Ca to P ratio is within the correct range, and by providing adequate levels of vitamin D3 either by exposure to UV-B

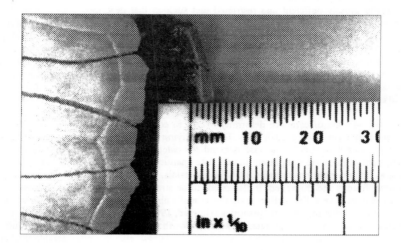

Above: Typical bone thickness and density as seen in the carapace of a wild adult *Testudo graeca*. The carapace of this specimen was smooth and showed no evidence of any developmental abnormality.

Above: Grossly abnormal bone thickness and density in a captive-bred *Testudo graeca*. The carapace of this specimen was severely distorted and exhibited profound 'pyramiding'. The bone is porous, fibrous and fragile. The keratin outer layer was thickened and dark in color. The diet of this tortoise had included a high percentage of canned dog food, without calcium supplementation. There was concurrent kidney disease - the immediate cause of death.

or via oral supplementation (Highfield, in preparation). It should be stressed that even on a generally grossly deficient and restricted diet such as that described above, normal bone growth can be achieved if supplementation with calcium, magnesium and other bone-building minerals is provided in conjunction with a source of vitamin D3 (Highfield, pers. obs.). It is notable that in nature, many tortoise species actively seek out additional sources of calcium, including sun-bleached bones and mineral rich soils (Schulkin, 1995, Esque and Peters, 1994). The present author has observed *Testudo graeca graeca* in Morocco and *Testudo kleinmanni* in Egypt consume vacated desert snail shells which are plentiful in such arid environments.

The second class of carapace deformity occurs in conjunction with high protein diets and consequent accelerated growth rates. The underlying cause is the same, however. The high growth rates dramatically increase demand for calcium and other bon-building trace elements and if these are not present in adequate quantity a state of deficiency will quickly occur, as bone deposition outstrips available materials. In response, the bony tissue becomes porous, fibrous and thickened. It also needs to be stressed that absolute high protein intake can and does have a direct effect upon the animal's ability to absorb calcium even when it is present in the diet in adequate quantities (Holford, 1997, Robbins,1983.). Furthermore, high protein intakes promote high rates of keratin growth (Robbins, op. cit.) and this results not only in a visible overgrowth of beak and nail material, but also in a considerable thickening of the outer (keratin) layer of the carapace. Typically, such animals manifest a melanistic appearance due to the darker, thicker layer of keratin overlying the intermediate membrane and underlying bony structures. Where keratin growth exceeds the rate of exponential growth of underlying bone, physical stresses are created that further tend to create distortion and abnormal patterns of growth (Highfield, unpublished data). One additional and little realized side-effect of unnaturally high rates of keratin growth and consequent melanization is that the tortoises' thermoregulatory abilities are severely impacted. The darkened carapace absorbs more radiant heat than would occur following normal growth and coloration (Highfield, 1999) and this affects both a) permissible activity levels in high temperatures and b) elevates the average body temperature with further dramatic consequences for microbial fermentation and overall digestive efficiency (Lichtenbelt, 1992). Although not directly relevant to the topic of carapace deformity and bone development, it is also very important to note that herbivores raised on high protein diets have dramatically reduced life expectancy due to premature renal failure and very high incidences of articular and visceral gout and bladder calculi of uric acid origin (Donoghue, S. in Mader, 1996, Highfield, 1990, 1996, 1999, MacArthur, 1996). There is a direct and absolute correlation between protein intake and uric acid generation (Schmidt-Nielsen, 1990). Commercial tortoise foods and vitamin or mineral supplements that include separate amino acids (e.g., lysine, leucine, trytophan or arginine, etc.) are best avoided as these have been associated with liver and kidney damage, gout, and calcium loss in human patients studied (Nantow and Heslin, 1997).

Protein
The precise protein demand of tortoises and herbivorous lizards is rather more difficult to calculate than for mammals due to their employment of microbial fermentation and their ectothermic nature (Alderman and Cottrill, 1993, Bjorndal, op. cit.) but nonetheless useful comparisons and conclusions can be drawn (Highfield: Feeding Herbivorous Lizards [in preparation], Troyer, 1984). It is also very informative to draw a direct comparison with typical human needs. For an average 70 kg, 25 year-old male, the estimated daily protein requirement is circa 44 grams, or 0.628 grams of useable protein per Kg of body weight. All available evidence suggests that very few, if any, omnivorous or herbivorous animals have

needs or typical consumption in excess of this (Carpenter, 1994, Robbins, 1983). We may therefore usefully consider this an absolute maximum figure on a gram per kg basis. If we then take a 2 kg (4.4 pound) tortoise, we find that its net useable protein requirement is in the order of a *maximum* of 1.25 grams of protein per day - or around one twentieth of one ounce! A requirement which is very easily met from typical consumed quantities of practically all available foods.

Raw protein percentage intake in nature is extremely low on a wet basis and in practice consumption is also limited by the physical capacity of the gut. Dry weight protein contents of foods that constitute 80-90% of the natural forage of *Gopherus agassizi* are given in table one where a comparison is also drawn with common substitute foods.

It should be noted that not only are the protein contents of many common substitute foods substantially higher than naturally consumed food plants, but their fat contents are also higher on average, and their fiber contents are considerably lower. This is further compounded by far less favorable Ca:P ratios.

Basal protein content of tortoise diets varies according to species, with arid habitat species typically adapted to lower overall protein intakes than humid habitat species due to renal function limitations and general food type availability constraints (Highfield, 1999, Schmidt-Nielsen, op. cit.). It is highly instructive to note that there is a direct correlation between habitat types (humid vs. arid), free water availability, and food preferences and protein intake in turtles and tortoises (Moyle, 1949). See table two. According to clinical data and nutritional histories collated by The Tortoise Trust, provision of excessive protein levels and types to unsuitable species will almost *invariably* result in renal damage if sustained.

There is a further direct correlation between habitat types, diet and the energy content of typical dietary constituents.

Carbohydrates and energy

Plant carbohydrates are typically polymers of five- and six-carbon monosaccharides. These can usefully be divided into structural and non-structural categories based upon their composition, position and function. The two most important structural carbohydrates of plants are cellulose and hemicellulose. There are substantial and relevant differences between plant carbohydrates when considering herbivorous reptile nutrition. The differences between the carbohydrate content of the diet of a tropical rain forest species that consumes a high proportion of fruit and an arid habitat species that primarily consumes grasses and flowers is striking (see table three). One important difference between typical structural and non-structural carbohydrates is that cellulose is not digested by vertebrates without the assistance of symbiotic gut microflora. By comparison, starch is easily digestible. Tortoises are able to extract a high proportion of their general nutrient and energy needs from very low quality plant fibers and cell wall materials using microbial ('hind-gut', proximal-colon or caecum-like) digestive processes (Bjorndal, op. cit., Highfield, 1990). Hemicelluloses are mostly polymers of five-carbon sugars, although six-carbon sugars such as glucose also exist. Hemicellulose is hydrolizable in both acid and alkaline environments, so is at least partially digested by stomach acids (Robbins, 1983). Pectin is another important structural carbohydrate. Pectin is far more concentrated in fruits than it is in grasses. Pectins are readily digested by symbiotic bacterial and protozoan gut flora.

39

TABLE 1

Comparison between natural major forage items of the Desert tortoise (*Gopherus agassizi*) and common substitute foods in captivity.

Natural Graze	% Protein (DM)	Crude Fiber	% Ca	%P	Ca:P
Foxtail Brome	8.5	31.6	0.28	0.23	1.2:1
Globemallow	20.4	23.2	3.34	0.31	10.8:1
Opuntia sp.	7.0	9.3	6.29	0.08	78.7:1
Fluffgrass	7.6	29.1	0.99	0.06	16..5:1
Muhly bush	7.3	36.9	0.27	0.09	3.0:1
Threeawn	6.3	34.8	0.59	0.09	6.6:1
Slim Tridens	9.1	34.1	0.61	0.17	3.6:1
Plantago sp.	13.3	15.9	4.16	0.19	21.9:1

Captive Diet	% Protein (DM)	Crude Fiber	% Ca	%P	Ca:P
Lettuce, Iceberg	22.00	11.1	0.44	0.44	1:1
Mustard Greens	28.5	10.5	1.74	0.48	3.6:1
Swiss Chard	27.0	9.0	0.99	0.44	2.3:1
Kale	34.6	7.5	1.44	0.54	2.7:1
Tomatoes	15.4	9.2	0.18	0.38	0.5:1
Cantaloupe	7.8	6.8	0.16	0.18	0.9:1
Endive	25.7	11.4	1.17	0.78	1.5:1
Green beans	19.3	14.1	0.57	0.44	1.3:1

Note the extreme disparity in protein levels, crude fiber content and average Ca:P ratios between wild and captive dietary components. *Values from Jarchow (1984)*

TABLE 2

Table correlating balance of nitrogenous products excreted by species from different environments and habitat classes (after Moyle, 1949).

Species	Habitat	Uric acid	Ammonia	Urea
K. subrubum	Aquatic	0.7	24.00	22.9
Pelusios sp.	Aquatic	4.5	18.5	24.4
E. orbicularis	Semi-aquatic	2.5	14.4	47.1
Kinixys erosa	Moist forests	4.2	6.1	61.00
Kinixys belliana	Drier habitats	5.5	6.00	44.00
G. denticulata	Moist forests	6.7	6.00	29.1
G. elegans	Semi arid	56.1	6.2	8.5
Testudo graeca	Semi-arid	51.9	4.1	22.3

Note to table two: Chelonia from habitats where water is plentiful are predominately aminoureoletic, excreting a combination of ammonia and urea, while tortoises from arid environments are predominantly uricotelic, excreting uric acid and urates.

TABLE 3

Average Carbohydrate Content of Grass, Flower and Leaf Forage (*Gopherus agassizi* and *Geochelone pardalis*) vs. High Fruit Content Diet (*Geochelone denticulata*)

Food Mixture	Average % Fat	Average % Carbohydrate
Natural foods of *G. agassizi*	2.2	45.5
Natural foods of *G. denticulata*	3.2	67.5
Natural foods of *G. pardalis*	2.5	48.5

Note to table three: There are several additional major differences between the diets of humid habitat and rain forest species, and semi-arid savannah habitat species, including, but not limited to; average moisture content of foods, protein content, pectin content and overall digestibility. Humid habitat species tend to consume foods that are digested more readily, and that have a lower overall fiber content. Because these humid habitat species also consume more in the way of carrion, the saturated fat content of their diets tends to be elevated compared to entirely herbivorous savannah species.

Non-structural carbohydrates include sucrose in fruits and plant sap, to starch in seeds and roots. These are found in all plant parts, but the highest concentrations occur in fruits, seeds, stems and roots. The precise content varies enormously, not only with seasons and general growth cycles, but also as a function of photosynthesis. Levels are higher late in the day than they are in early morning, for example (Robbins, 1983)

In purely practical terms, one implication is that the feeding of high quantities of fruit to those species where this is not a natural dietary items (e.g., mostly arid habitat and savannah habitat tortoises) can have the effect of seriously accelerating gut motility, increasing gas production (tympany), altering gut pH, and severely disturbing normal digestive processes and symbiotic microflora balance. Conversely, attempting to maintain those species adapted to readily digestible high starch and pectin intakes on grasses could result in a serious energy deficit.

Carbohydrates represent the prime energy source in herbivorous reptile diets. Excess intake can be stored either as glycogen in the liver, or as fat (reserves of these substances are critical in those species that hibernate). Excess intake of readily fermentable carbohydrates and sugars in species ill-adapted for such diets can, however, result in profound disturbance to the animal's entire metabolism. In cattle and horses, ruminal acidosis is a well-known phenomenon (Nocek, 1991, Stock and Britton, 1991). Specific pathologies associated with this condition include:

- Clostridial infections
- Laminitis
- Liver abscesses
- Malabsorbtion syndrome resulting from ruminal wall tissue damage
- Sudden death syndrome
- Diarrhea and dehydration

TABLE 4

Food values of legumes and soy products compared to live crickets

All legumes fresh unless otherwise stated. Snap beans are lowest in protein and carbohydrate as seed component is immature and not developed as consumed. The phytic acid content remains high at 4,800 ppm, however, reducing the availability of the apparently good calcium content.

Item (100g)	Protein (g)	Calories	Carbohydrate	P (mg)	C (mg)
Crickets, live	12.9	121	5.1	183.5	78.5
Broad beans	8.4	105	17.8	157	27
Lima beans	8.4	123	22.1	142	52
Soya beans	10.9	134	13.2	225	67
Peas (frozen)	5.0	68	12.0	86	19
Peas	6.3	84	14.4	116	26
Snap beans	1.2	22	4.9	14	54
Tofu, firm	14.5	135	6.8	60	18.5

It should be noted that the digestive mechanism of tortoises and herbivorous lizards is functionally identical to those of commercial ruminants. The etiology of the condition is that starch-rich foods (cereal grains, corn, for example) are broken down into sugars (glucose) in the digestive tract. Alternatively, sugar-rich foods are metabolized directly and very rapidly (quantities of fresh, sweet grass or fruit, for example). In the hind-gut, symbiotic bacteria ferment the carbohydrates to form volatile fatty acids (VFA's) which are absorbed and are an important source of energy, representing, on average, between 30-40% of total requirements in some herbivorous reptiles studied (McBee and McBee, 1982, Troyer, 1984b). Very high intakes of carbohydrates such as starches and sugars can overwhelm the system, however, and ferment much more quickly than the fiber contained in dry grasses and hays. The result is a massive increase in acids produced by bacterial action. These acids are primarily acetic, propionic and butyric acid with lower levels of lactic acid and VFA's (McBee and McBee, 1982). Following over-consumption of starches and sugars the pH of the gut shifts to become highly acidic initiating a chain of serious consequences (typical gut pH ranges of herbivorous reptiles are in the order of 6.8-7.0). One particularly serious effect is the generation of high levels of endotoxins produced as the normal symbiotic and commensal gut bacteria begin to die in the out-of-range acidic environment created (approximately pH <5.5). The gut wall integrity can begin to degrade in these conditions, causing subsequent malabsorbtion of nutrients. Liver abscessing is a typical consequence of this condition as bacteria are absorbed into the bloodstream via the gut wall, and seed themselves in the liver. In this context it is important to take note of the fact that liver diseases are one of the most common causes of death in captive arid habitat chelonia, representing up to 72.6% of all mortalities studied (Rosskopf, Howard, Gendron, Walder, and Britt, 1981). Some of the foods most commonly associated with causing severe gastric disruption (including sudden death) in arid habitat and savannah species in captivity include peaches, plums, pears and apples - all of which are very high in easily digestible soluble carbohydrates and fruit sugars. Species that appear particularly susceptible to such problems include:

- Leopard tortoises (*Geochelone pardalis*)
- African Spurred tortoises (*Geochelone sulcata*)
- Mediterranean *Testudo* species
- Russian tortoise (*Testudo horsfieldii*)
- Indian Star tortoises (*Geochelone elegans*)
- North American *Gopherus* species
- South African *Homopus*, *Psammobates* and *Chersina* species
- Pancake tortoises (*Malacochersus tornieri*)
- Radiated tortoises (*Geochelone radiata*)

The condition is preventable by providing appropriate diets. A table of commonly maintained species and their requirements in this respect is given on page 44. High fiber, low grain content, low carbohydrate (low fruit sugar) foods are appropriate to most arid habitat and savannah species, while many humid habitat tropical species have a natural tolerance to higher intakes of sugars and carbohydrates (though with lowered tolerance to, and less ability to digest, silica-rich grasses compared to savannah species). All species typically benefit from high to very high fiber intakes. *High fiber intakes are one of the most effective practical measures to prevent acidosis in susceptible species.*

TABLE 5

Dietary Requirements for Species Commonly Maintained in Captivity

Species	Basic Diet	Notes
Geochelone pardalis **Leopard tortoise**	Mixed grasses, flowers and succulent plants.	Excess intake of fruits is problematic. Provide only very occasionally.
Geochelone sulcata **African Spurred tortoise**	As above.	Makes extensive use of burrow microclimates. Do not provide fruit.
Geochelone elegans **Indian Star tortoise**	As above.	Experiences wet and dry seasons throughout much of range.
Testudo graeca, T. ibera **Spur-thighed tortoise**	Mixed flowers, succulent plants and green leaves.	Fruit and carbohydrate rich diets problematic.
Testudo kleinmanni **Egyptian tortoise**	Mixed flowers, succulent plants and green leaves.	Estivates in summer in the wild. Sandy habitats. Fruit problematic.
Trachemys scripta elegans **Red-Eared Slider turtle**	Carnivorous as a juvenile, progressing to largely herbivorous (aquatic plants) as adult.	Almost entirely aquatic leaving water only to bask and nest.
Testudo hermanni **Hermann's tortoise**	Mixed flowers, green-leaf material.	Diet ranges from 'wet' in spring to quite high percentage of dry vegetation later.
Testudo horsfieldii **Russian tortoise**	Mixed flowers and green leaves. Avoid fruit.	Tendency to overfeed in captivity. Very short natural activity cycle.
Geochelone carbonaria **Red-footed tortoise**	Fruits, flowers, green-leaf material and some animal protein.	Cannot digest large volumes of grasses.
Terrapene carolina **American box turtle**	Live prey, fallen fruits, mushrooms.	Moist habitats, secretive, feed at dusk and dawn.
Kinixys homeana **Home's Hinge-back tortoise**	As above. Millipedes and snails are favorites.	As above.
Cuora galbinifrons **Flower-back box turtle**	As above. In captivity waxworms, crickets and mealworms are accepted.	Very moist habitats. Semi-aquatic. Soaking pool required.
Indotestudo elongata **Elongate tortoise**	Flowers, green-leaf material, some fallen fruits, occasional carrion.	Occurs in both humid and relatively dry habitats.

It is vital, however, not to attempt to raise dietary fiber levels by including bran (very high phytic acid levels) or oats (exceptionally high phytic acid and carbohydrate levels). Bread is also particularly bad on both counts (as well as being extremely high in fat). Corn is also excludable due to high carbohydrate and phytic acid levels. Meadow and orchard hays represent the most acceptable form of supplemental fiber for most semi-arid and savannah tortoise species. Many *Geochelone, Gopherus* and *Testudo* species naturally experience a shift toward drier, hay-type foods as the moist spring advances towards the dry summer season. At such times, the availability high moisture-content spring annuals declines sharply, and instead tortoises are observed to pick at dry leaves, stems, dry flower heads and seed pods.

The total calorific or gross energy content of a food is dependent upon many factors. Carnivores may expect to obtain from 0.5-2.5 kcal/gram of whole prey animal consumed. Whole fish, as consumed by an aquatic turtle, range from 0.8 kcal/g to 2.5 kcal/g, for example. Insectivorous reptiles typically obtain from 0.6 kcal/g to 2.2 kcal/g from their diets. The energy content of certain live foods consumed by some tropical tortoises, such as Hingebacks (*Kinixys* sp.) or Red-foot tortoises (*Geochelone carbonaria*) is quite low. Snails, for example may have an energy content as low as 0.1 kcal/g - although their calciferous shell offers other dietary advantages.

Plant foods are highly variable in kcal content (see table six), and the efficiency with which this is utilized is also highly variable in ectothermic reptilian herbivores. A number of authors have attempted to study and quantify this, across a range of species (Robinson, 1995, Bjorndal and Bolton, 1993, Troyer, 1984b, Foley, et. al., 1992, Avery and Neibergs, 1997, Waller and Micucci, 1997). The energy needs of herbivorous reptiles approximates that of their protein needs, in that it is surprisingly low. A 1 kilogram (2.2 pound) Dhab lizard, *Uromastyx aegyptius*, for example, can easily survive on approximately 11.8 kcal per day, roughly equivalent to just 3.7 grams of typically consumed natural vegetation. A smaller individual, weighing 65 g (2.1 ounces), would require only 550 kcal or 0.17 grams of food (Robinson, 1995) to meet its total energy expenditure. Average daily intakes are usually 2.3 to 2.7 times this bare minimum (Foley, et. al, 1992) but the resulting food volumes still remain astonishingly low. For *Iguana iguana* the daily kcal expenditures range from 5.48 kcal at 28°C to 14.26 kcal at 35°C (Baer and Oftedal, 1995).

TABLE 6

Average Energy Content of Plant Parts and Communities
Source: Golley, 1961

Plant part or community	Average energy content (kcak/g)
Green leaves	4.229
Stems and branches	4.267
Roots	4.720
Seeds	5.065
Herbs (old field)	4.177
Perennial grasses	3.905
Tropical rain forest	3.897

Feeding frequency, quality and growth

In general terms, given a stable and unchanging basal formulation, a tortoise fed larger quantities of any given diet will in effect receive larger amounts of protein and carbohydrates than an animal fed lesser amounts. If 50 grams of food containing 0.5g of raw protein is given to tortoise 'A', and 100 grams of the same food is fed to tortoise 'B', tortoise 'B' will have consumed twice the protein consumed by tortoise 'A' (1g vs. 0.5g). Feeding quantity therefore directly impacts overall protein intake. The feeding of dry pelleted foods is problematic in this respect, as their protein content tend to be rather high (typically circa 20%) and gut volume is not as effective a limiting factor as it is with lower protein, bulkier foods. Tortoises simply eat a similar quantity of these concentrated foods as they would if a natural, less concentrated food was supplied. *The net effect is a massive increase in overall protein consumption, a rise in urate production, and an accelerated rate of growth.*

It is commonplace for captive hatched siblings to develop at different rates. Upon investigation, it is usually found to be the case that the individuals are engaging in very different feeding behaviors, often due to dominance and competition (Highfield, pers. obs.) or temperature differentials within the captive environment. Food quality and net protein availability also dramatically influences growth rates achieved (Highfield, 1990, 1996).

It has frequently been noted that tortoises from arid and extreme environments have a greater tendency to 'pyramid' or present with carapace deformities in captivity than those from less arid zones. Examples of the former include *Geochelone pardalis, Geochelone chilensis, Geochelone elegans, Testudo kleinmanni,* and *Testudo horsfieldii*. Examples of the latter include *Geochelone denticulata, Kinixys belliana* and *Geochelone elephantopus.* Some reflection upon the nature of these environments is useful. There is a direct and immediate correlation between tortoises from zones with dramatic seasonal shifts in availability of vegetation and their tendency to 'pyramid' in captivity. Tortoises from zones with more stable vegetation cycles tend to exhibit fewer such problems (pers. obs.). In captivity, animals from arid zones tend to feed on a much more continuous basis than they would in nature. During drought and vegetation deprivation cycles in nature, wild tortoises in arid habitats reduce their energy needs dramatically (50-80%) by remaining inactive in burrows for very extended periods (Nagy, 1998). In captivity, these deprivation cycles are not present as limiting factors. As a result, within, for example, any 12 month period, their overall food consumption is many times greater than would be achieved by a wild counterpart (Highfield, 1999). This equates directly to an overall increase in protein consumed and consequently higher growth rates and a greater demand for calcium and other bone-building trace elements over the same period. Where deficiencies of calcium and related materials occur, this naturally results in a far greater propensity to manifest with fibrous osteodystrophy related deformities. Calcium demand in tortoises increases in line with rates of growth, and, in the case of females, with egg development. An effective calcium to phosphorus ratio is generally cited as 2:1 (Mader, 1996), although the present author feels that this really does represent a minimum rather than an optimum figure. This view was shared by Jarchow (1984). A suggested optimum figure in captivity would be in the order of 3 to 4 parts calcium to one part phosphorus on an applied basis (absorbed figures are lower due to interference from anti-nutrient secondary plant compounds including oxalates, phytates, etc., and the inefficient rate at which calcium is absorbed from food). Many natural foods of tortoises feature very high Ca:P ratios - as high as 78.7:1 in the case of the Prickly pear cactus, *Opuntia* sp., although a more representative figure is in the region of 5:1 to 8:1. There is strong evidence that mammalian ruminants are able to self-regulate absorption of Ca from the gut according to need and that they can also alter the efficiency of absorption in order to meet a change in requirement (McDowell, 1989). It is probable that tortoises, turtles and other herbivorous reptiles possess a similar control mechanism. Clinical cases of direct dietary calcium excess are extraordinarily rare, and there is typically an aggravating co-factor. Frye (1993) states "Only where accompanied by an excess of vitamin D3 is an over abundance of calcium a problem".

It should be clearly noted that an excess consumption of low protein plant foods is just as likely to result in excess growth and deformity as consumption of lower amounts of intrinsically higher protein foods, such as meat products or monkey chow. High protein, high purine plant-derived foods such as peas, beans or tofu are just as damaging as any animal product, not only in terms of generating artificially accelerated growth, but also in terms of their capacity to cause elevated blood urea nitrogen levels and consequent articular and visceral gout in the longer term. In addition, many such foods contain damaging substances including phytic and oxalic acids that further inhibit calcium availability and uptake (Highfield, 1988 and present volume, NIH, 1994). Peas and beans in particular are especially poor in this respect. Compare the protein and calcium levels of typical legumes and soy products with live crickets, for example (table four). The argument that while animal foods are damaging to herbivorous tortoises, high protein vegetable foods are inherently "safe" is clearly erroneous. There is little practical difference - and some vegetable based foods, notably tofu, are substantially higher in protein content than some foods of animal origin. Although lentils and sprouted beans and peas have been recommended as safe and nutritious foods for herbivorous reptiles (Frye, 1993) they are contra-indicated for the reasons cited, and in practice have resulted not only in a high incidence of carapace deformity in hatchlings, but also in renal failure and bladder calculi in many species (Tortoise Trust, unpublished veterinary and pathology records).

The effect of temperature
The primary environmental effect upon feeding and growth is temperature. Higher temperatures tend to promote increased feeding and activity in reptiles. This in turn results in higher overall protein intakes, that in turn results in higher rates of growth. A secondary, but critical effect, is that higher temperatures greatly increase microbial fermentation productivity and efficiency. For example, the uptake of glucose in the intestines increases with temperature as does the breakdown of structural carbohydrates due to microbial degradation. Gut transit times in herbivorous reptiles are also greatly accelerated by higher temperatures (Harlow, Hillman and Hoffman, 1976, Lichtenbelt, 1992, Zimmerman and Tracy, 1989). Overall digestive coefficients have also been noted to increase from 54.3% at 33°C to 69.5% at 41°C in the herbivorous lizard *Disosaurus dorsalis* (Harlow, Hillman and Hoffman, op. cit.) although this study is open to criticism due to the force-feeding techniques employed. There is considerable evidence, however, that many other lizards and turtles certainly employ a raised-temperature strategy as juveniles to enhance nutrient extraction from microbial fermentation processes (Bjorndal, op.cit., Troyer, op. cit, McBee and McBee, 1982). By maintaining captive tortoises at higher temperatures it is therefore entirely reasonable to suppose that their overall digestive coefficients are enhanced and that this directly results in higher rates of growth in addition to an increased behavioral preference for feeding at higher temperatures typical of all reptiles. This is certainly borne out by numerous anecdotal reports from keepers, and by personal observations over many years.

Environment and nutrition in herbivorous ectotherms are essentially inseparable. The net consequence is that elevated temperatures result in high rates of feeding (up to a certain point, at which feeding decreases and the animal seeks shelter or enters estivation), higher rates of digestive coefficient, and faster gut transit times. These factors in turn result in higher rates of overall growth and enhanced demand for calcium and other bone-building trace elements. Should these not be available, deficiencies will manifest in the form of fibrous osteodystrophy and visible carapace deformity. Where they are provided at an adequate level to keep pace with the high rates of growth being attained, smooth carapace growth can be successfully achieved, though not without some cost to the renal system as a result of the higher levels of serum urea generated.

The effect of water availability, humidity and hydration status
The second major environmental factor to be considered is water availability and humidity. Where high protein intakes are being consumed, and high rates of growth consequently attained, blood urea levels will typically be elevated. Visible output of urates will also increase and greater fluid intakes are required in order to evacuate these effectively. Dehydration is a particular hazard to reptiles, and especially those maintained on high protein diets (Highfield, 1987, 1988b). Aquarium tank-type vivaria are rarely appropriate for terrestrial tortoises, and frequently result in dehydration and other health problems. Open-topped indoor and outdoor terraria are a far superior option. Provision of correct microclimates (scrapes, burrows and suitable substrate) can play a major role in preventing dehydration from evaporative losses via skin and respiration (Highfield, 1999, 1999b, Highfield and Bayley, 1996, Nagy, 1998) but is insufficient alone to prevent urate deposition and concentration from occurring, giving rise to various forms of gout. Adequate fresh water must be available in quantities to supply the renal system's needs in order to successfully evacuate the amount of nitrogenous waste being generated. This typically coincides with summer thunderstorms in desert habitats (Nagy, op. cit., Highfield, pers. obs.). Water demand increases with both raw quantity of food consumed and in direct relationship to the protein (and purine) content of the diet. Where animals are fed on a higher protein diet, it is thus essential that their hydration status is fully maintained at an adequate level. Many arid habitat species will only evacuate urates when a fresh water source is immediately available (pers. obs.), presumably as a water conservation strategy. Urination and the elimination of urate separation products can frequently be initiated in such animals by soaking in a shallow pool or by spraying to simulate rain. Such practices will considerably reduce the possibility of bladder calculi and renal failure - although by far the most effective method is to moderate and control overall feeding behavior and protein intake in the first place combined with adequate fluid availability and microclimate provision. It is open to speculation what other effects environmental water, or the lack thereof, may have upon feeding, growth and development. There is a possibility that in some situations nitrogenous wastes may be absorbed and used by symbiotic gut flora in turtles and tortoises as they are in certain mammalian herbivores - but direct evidence for this is lacking. Many arid habitat reptiles certainly conserve and recycle bladder contents (Frye, 1993, Dantzler and Schmidt-Nielson, 1966), and it is possible that some nitrogenous products are re-absorbed simultaneously. Though the concentrations are relatively low, water may also contain calcium (typically from 30 mg to 100 mg per liter), and it is therefore possible that consumption of water could have some slight impact upon overall calcium availability. Lack of water will certainly tend to suppress feeding after a certain period and will also slow down gut transit times of previously consumed materials.

One interesting aspect of the environment-development interface that requires further investigation is the possible impact of localized humidity upon rapidly growing keratin. Keratin is a fibrous protein formed of coiled polypeptide chains that are combined into supercoils of several polypeptides linked by disulphide bonds between adjacent cysteine amino acids. Aggregates of these supercoils form microfibrils which are embedded in a protein matrix. The resulting structure is strong, but relatively elastic. Keratin is also hygroscopic - to the extent that for many years human hair was employed in laboratory humidity measuring equipment as the sensor mechanism. Hair comprises dead keratin cells, while the keratin of a tortoise's shell is living, however, there is undoubtedly a differential in the fluid content between inner and outer surfaces (even though the thickness involved is only a fraction of a millimeter) especially in hot, arid environments). It has been noted that carapace 'pyramiding' tends to be worse when animals are reared at high growth rates in very dry as opposed to the same rate of growth in more humid environments. It is interesting to speculate upon the possible mechanisms for this. The most probable cause is that the fluid content differential in very dry environments creates physical stresses within the keratin layer that have the effect of exerting influence upon the rapidly developing (and relatively plastic) underlying bone. It is very important to note that this effect is only liable to manifest in situations where very rapid growth rates caused by high protein diets are present. Such diets promote not only rapid growth generally, but also result in considerable acceleration of keratin production as noted earlier. These would represent the ideal conditions for such an effect to manifest. It is also vital to note that none of the other consequences for health of high-protein intakes would in any way be ameliorated by increasing ambient humidity during such growth even though the most visible external effect known as 'pyramiding' may be reduced.

Conclusions

Feeding, growth and environment are inseparable in ectotherms. It is impossible to consider one factor without reference to others. In this sense, it is quite true to state that environment plays a critical role in growth and development. It does so, however, because it influences food intake, feeding behavior, and the way in which the consumed foods are processed. Bone structure and development is not *directly* affected by temperature, water or ambient humidity, and it is quite erroneous to assume any such direct link, save for the possible influence of humidity upon the keratin outer layer of a turtle's shell as discussed above. The primary causal factor of growth is food intake and utilization. Carapace deformities are caused by nutritional disorders. These disorders may be disorders of either excess or deficiency. While environment plays a role by influencing and affecting the metabolism of foods within the digestive tract, and by influencing the desire to feed, environment is not the direct cause of 'pyramiding' or 'lumpy shell syndrome' in chelonia any more than it is the direct cause of MBD in other herbivorous reptiles. The prime cause of 'pyramiding' or 'lumpy shell syndrome' is fibrous osteodystrophy resulting from excess rates growth combined with absolute or relative calcium and related trace-element deficiencies, vitamin D3 deficiencies, and excessive keratin growth that also result from high protein intakes over a period of time.

It is quickly evident, upon studying the wild dietary profiles of herbivorous tortoises, that meeting their needs in captivity is exceptionally difficult. Even the best efforts based upon 'supermarket produce' are unlikely to satisfy these animals very specialized requirements, although opportunistic omnivores such as rain forest species are generally easier to satisfy than exclusive herbivores from semi-arid and savannah habitats The most successful approach for these tortoises must be to cultivate 'semi-natural' grazing areas designed to accommodate each individual species nutritional and environmental needs. The cultivation of suitable forage and feeding plants must rank as a high priority for those who intend to keep these species in good health over the long-term and to raise successive healthy generations in captivity. Environmental temperatures need to be regulated in order to produce activity cycles that closely replicate the number of 'feeding days' that occur naturally, by use of hibernation and estivation where necessary. Pen and habitat design is critical, as is the provision of appropriate microclimates.

Perfect and natural growth in tortoises can be achieved by restricting absolute or relative protein intake, by providing adequate amounts of calcium and other essential trace elements, by ensuring adequate availability of vitamin D3 and by encouraging 'rest' periods to break the pattern of continuous feeding so typical of captive animals i.e., by avoiding over-heating, consequent over-feeding, and artificially extended activity cycles.

It is certainly the case that apparently healthy 'smooth' tortoises can be grown very quickly on relatively high protein diets provided certain conditions are met, but this is not without grave risk in terms of long-term survivability (Highfield, 1997, 1999). The renal status of such animals is questionable at best and there are further implications for hepatic condition.

Acknowledgements: The author would like to thank Dr. Chris Tabaka, D.V.M. for critical review and for proof-reading this text. Thanks are also due to Jill Martin, my co-founder at Tortoise Trust, for her work on developing practical diets for many of the species discussed, for gathering data on growth and development, for collating case histories, and for the excellent standard of daily care accorded to all animals that reside there. Thanks also to Lin King and Ashley Woods for sharing their own information and techniques.

References:

Alderman, G. and Cottrill, B. R. (1993) Energy and Protein Requirements of Ruminants. CAB International, Oxford.

Avery, H. W. (1989) Role of diet, protein and temperature in the nutritional energetics of the turtle, *Trachemys scripta*: Implications for the nutritional ecology of the Desert tortoise. Desert Tortoise Council. Proc. 1987-1991 Symposia: 160.

Baer, D. J. and Oftedal, O. T. (1995) Effects of Temperature on Nutrient Utilization in Herbivorous Reptiles. Desert Tortoise Council. Proc. 1995 Symposium:54-55.

Bjorndal, K.A. (1985) Nutritional ecology of the sea turtle. Copeia 1985:736-751.

Bjorndal, K.A. (1987) Digestive efficiency in a temperate herbivorous reptile, *Gopherus polyphemus*. Copieia 1987:714-720.

Bjorndal, K. A., and Bolten, A. (1993) Digestive Efficiencies in Herbivorous and Omnivorous Freshwater Turtles on Plant Diets: Do Herbivores have a Nutritional Advantage? Physiol. Zool. 66(3):384-395.

Carpenter, K. J. (1994) Protein and Energy: A study of changing ideas in nutrition. Cambridge U.P.

Cooper, J. E., and Jackson, O.F. (1981) (eds). Diseases of the Reptilia. Academic Press. London.

Dantzler, W.H, and Schmidt-Nielson, B., (1966) Excretion in the freshwater turtle (*Pseudemys scripta*) and the Desert tortoise (*Gopherus agassizii*). Am. J. Physiology. 198-210.

Donoghue, S. and Langenberg, J. (1995) Clinical Nutrition of Exotic Pets. Veterinary Clinical Nutrition 2 (2):57-63.

Esque, T. C. and Peters, E. L. (1994) Ingestion of bones, stones and soil by Desert tortoises. Fish and Wildlife Research 13:105-111.

Fife, Richard (2000) Protein does not cause pyramiding. Kingsnake Forum Post.

Foley, W. J., Bouskila, A., Shkolnik, A., and Chosniak, I. (1992) Microbial digestion in the herbivorous lizard, *Uromastyx aegyptius* (Agamidae). J. Zool. Soc. Lond. (226):387-398.

Frye, F. (1993) A Practical Guide for Feeding Captive Reptiles. Kreiger, Malabar, Florida.

Golley, F. B. (1961) Energy Values of Ecological Materials. Ecology 42:581-584

Harlow, H. J., Hillman, S. S., and Hoffman, M. (1976) The effect of temperature on digestive efficiency in the herbivorous lizard, *Dipsosaurus dorsalis*. J. Comp. Physiology. B111:1-6.

Harris, D. M. (1982) The Phenology, Growth and Survival of the Green Iguana *Iguana iguana* in Northern Columbia. in: Iguanas of the World, their Behaviour, Ecology, and Conservation. Eds. Burghardt, G. M. and Rand, A.S. Noyes Publications, NJ.

Highfield, A. C. (1988) Notes on Dietary Constituents for Herbivorous Terrestrial Chelonia and their Effect on Growth and Development. ASRA. Reprinted in: The Feeding Manual, Tortoise Trust,. London.

Highfield, A. C. (1988b) Husbandry Notes: Observations on Dehydration in Reptiles. The Rephiberary nr. 131.

Highfield, A. C. (1987) Causal Factors of Mortality in Captive Collections. Testudo 2(5):15-17.

Highfield, A. C. (1990) Keeping & Breeding Tortoises in Captivity. R&A Publications, Bristol.

Highfield, A. C. (1996) Practical Encyclopedia of Keeping and Breeding Tortoises and Freshwater Turtles, Carapace Press, London.

Highfield, A. C. (1999b) Practical Care of Mediterranean (Greek) Tortoises. Carapace Press Vidi-Herp Series, London and NJ.

Highfield, A. C. and Bayley, J. R. (1996) Observations on ecological changes threatening a population of *Testudo graeca graeca* in the Souss Valley, southern Morocco. Chelonian Conservation and Biology 2(1):36-42.

Highfield, A. C. (1997) High growth rates and vitamin D3 - a response. The Tortuga Gazette (33)12:8-9.

Highfield, A. C. (1999) Feeding Your Tortoise. Carapace Press Video. London.

Jackson, G. and Trotter, J.A., T.H., and M.W, (1967). Herpetologica 32:139-145.

Jackson, O. and Fasal, M. D. (1981) Radiology in tortoises and turtles as an aid to diagnosis. J. Small Anim. Pract. 22:705-716.

Jarchow, J. L. (1984) Veterinary Management of the Desert Tortoise, *Gopherus agassizii,* at the Arizona-Sonora Desert Museum: A rational approach to diet. Gopher Tortoise Council, Proceedings 1984 Symposium: 83-94.

Holford, P. (1997) The Optimum Nutrition Bible. Piatkus, London.

Lambert, M. R. K. (1986) On the Growth of captive-bred Mediterranean Testudo in N. Europe. In: Studies in Herpetology, 309-314. Prague: Charles University.

King, G. (1996) Reptiles and Herbivory. Chapman and Hall.

Lichtenbelt, W. D. van Marken (1992). Digestion in an Ectothermic Herbivore, the Green Iguana: Effect of Food Composition and Body Temperature. Physiological Zoology. (65):649-673.

McBee, R. H., and McBee, V. H. (1982) The Hindgut Fermentation in the Green Iguana, *Iguana iguana.* In: Iguanas of the World, their Behaviour, Ecology, and Conservation Eds. Burghardt, G.M. and Rand, A.S. Noyes Publications, NJ.

Meienberger, C. Wallis, I. R., and Nagy, K. A. (1993) Food intake rate and body mass influence transit time and digestibility in the desert tortoise (*Xerobates agassizii*). Physiol. Zool. (66):847-862.

Moyle (1949) cited in: Schmidt-Neilson, op. cit.

Nagy, K. A. (1998) Energy and Water requirements of juvenile and adult desert tortoises in the Mojave desert. *Lecture to:* International Conference on Tortoises and Turtles, Cal. State Univ. July 30 - Aug 2.

Nantow, A. B., and Heslin, J. (1997) The Protein Counter. Pocket Books, NY.

Iverson, J. B. (1982) Adaptions to Herbivory in Iguanine Lizards. In: Iguanas of the World, their Behaviour, Ecology, and Conservation. Eds. Burghardt, G.M. and Rand, A.S. Noyes Publications, NJ.

MacArthur, S. MRCVS (1996) Veterinary Management of Tortoises and Turtles. Blackwell Science, Oxford.

Mader, D. (1996) Reptile Medicine and Surgery. W.B. Saunders Company

McDowell, L. R. (1989) Vitamins in Animal Nutrition. Academic Press, London.

Moskovits, D. and Bjorndal, K. A. (1990) Diet and Food Preferences of the Tortoises Geochelone carbonaria and *G. denticulata* in Northwestern Brazil. Herpetologica 46(2):207-218.

Nocek, J. E. (1991) The link between Nutrition, Acidosis, Laminitis and Environment. Agway Research Centre, Tully, NY.

Pritchard, P. C. H and Trebbau, P. (1984) The Turtles of Venezuela. SSAR.

Robbins, Charles T. (1983). Wildlife Feeding and Nutrition. Academic Press. London.

Robinson, M. D. (1995) Food Plants and Energetics of the herbivorous lizards, *Uromastyx aegyptius microlepis,* in Kuwait. J. Univ. Kuwait (Sci.) 22:256-261.

Rosskopf, W. J. (1982) Severe shell deformity caused by a deficient diet in a California Desert Tortoise. Veterinary Medicine, Small Animal Clinician. April 1982.

Rosskopf, W. J., Howard, E, Gendron, A.P., Walder, E., and Britt, J. O (1981). Mortality studies on *Gopherus agassizi* and Gopherus berlandieri tortoises. Desert Tortoise Council. Proceedings 1981 Symposium 108-112.

Wallach, J. D. (1971). Environmental and Nutritional diseases of Captive Reptiles. J. Am. V. M. Assn. 159:1633-1643.

Schmidt-Nielsen, K. (1990) Animal Physiology: Adaptation and Environment. Cambridge University Press

Schulkin, J. (1995) Do Reptiles have Mineral Appetites? Desert Tortoise Council. Proc. 1995 Symposium:66-68

Solar, S. (1997) How to raise baby tortoises indoors. The Tortuga Gazette. (33)9:5-10.

Stock, R. and Britton, R. (1991) Acidosis. File G1047, A25, Cattle. US Dept. Agriculture.

Troyer, K. (1984) Structure and Function of the Digestive Tract of a Herbivorous Lizard, *Iguana iguana*. Physiological Zoology (57):1-8.

Troyer, K. (1984b) Diet selection and digestion in *Iguana iguana*: the importance of age and nutrient requirements. Oecologia (Berlin) 61:201-207.

Van Devender, R. W. (1982) Growth and Ecology of Spiny-tailed Iguanas in Costa Rica with comments on the Evolution of Herbivory and Large Body Size. In: Iguanas of the World, their Behaviour, Ecology, and Conservation. Eds. Burghardt, G.M. and Rand, A.S. Noyes Publications, NJ.

Waller, T. and Micucci, P. (1997) Land use and Grazing in relation to the Genus *Geochelone* in Argentina. Proc. Cons. Restoration and Management of Tortoises and Turtles. NYTTS, New York.

Zimmerman, L. C., and Tracy, C. R. (1989) Interactions between the environment and ectothermy and herbivory in reptiles. Physiol. Zool. 62(2):374-409.